Official Workbook

for

more than
a body

LINDSAY KITE PhD
& LEXIE KITE PhD

Page design by Robert Henry at Right Hand Publishing

Cover design by Kayli Timmerman

ISBN: 979-8-9895428-0-2

Published by More Than a Body LLC
To contact the publisher or find more resources,
visit www.morethanabody.org

Contents

Preface

"While your body image is not something that can be viewed or perceived from the outside, too many of us can't imagine our feelings about our bodies from any other perspective. This reveals a deeper problem with women's body images and self-worth than most people recognize, and one that popular 'You are beautiful!' body-image campaigns are not capable of solving: Women are privileging an external view of their bodies over their own internal, first-person perspective. It's as if we, as women, exist outside of ourselves—as if our bodies can be understood only through someone else's eyes."

—*More Than a Body*, p. 5-6

Since 2009, we—Lindsay and Lexie Kite, identical twins, body image researchers, and co-authors of *More Than a Body: Your body is an instrument, not an ornament* (Harper-Collins, 2020)—have been writing and speaking about body image and objectification. The number one question we get from both new and longtime followers of our work is, "How do I really do this?" People will often say things like, "I believe everything you've said and written about body image, and yet the self-conscious thoughts still creep in regularly and

I feel overwhelmed that I'm still dealing with this even after knowing I'm more than a body."

More than anything, we want people to know that these intrusive feelings of body shame and a desire to "fix" our bodies are not a reflection of our own weakness or inadequacy—physically, mentally, or spiritually. It is actually a reflection of the strength and severity of the body-obsessed ideals in our culture. These messages are so deeply rooted and widespread that they can counteract that deeper knowledge that our bodies are instruments, not ornaments. This workbook is our answer to that question of "but how?"

Building your body image resilience—or your ability to become more self-assured and at peace with your body because of the challenges you face—is an ongoing, continuous process. It's not a finish line you cross where the beauty pressures of your environment magically lose all their power. It is a muscle you develop and strengthen over time through deliberate, compassionate strategies that help you reconnect to your whole, embodied self each time you feel yourself start to slip into self-consciousness and body shame. This repeated choice to strengthen and flex your resilience muscles instead of coping with shame by hiding or fixing your body can eventually become second nature to you. The commitment of time and energy you put into these strategies will benefit you both immediately and in the long term as you learn to navigate the objectifying environment with greater ease and power.

It's important for us to note that all the resilience in the world can't make objectification just disappear or have no effect on you—it won't go away because it is profitable, and it maintains hierarchies that people in power rely on. Discrimination and bias based on size, shape, race, ethnicity, hair type, ability, gender, and gender identity are pervasive. Our solutions do not hinge on top-down solutions like legislation, petitions, or major industry oversight because we don't believe change will happen that way. Instead, we offer recommendations for individuals to navigate the harsh reality of the environment we live in while pushing back against the normalized objectification we've become numb to—first for ourselves and those we care about and then collectively spreading that knowledge and action beyond our immediate circles of influence. Instead of continuing to adapt to an unfair and unhealthy environment, we are asking you to join us in fighting for a better one.

Though our research has focused on girls, women, and those who identify as such, we acknowledge that boys, men, and people of all gender identities also struggle with body image issues. It is not our intention to exclude anyone, but rather to be clear about our specific research focus and findings. However, we strongly believe our work and the concepts and strategies presented in this workbook can be beneficial for anyone—regardless of gender, race, ability, socioeconomic status, or any other variable—who has felt uncomfortable in their body due to the harmful appearance ideals and pressures in our looks-obsessed world.

This workbook is designed as a companion to our book, *More Than a Body: Your body is an instrument, not an ornament*, to equip you with practical steps and challenges that will help build your body image resilience. Structured similarly to the six chapters of *More Than a Body*, we have broken some of the most important concepts into four weekly, bite-sized lessons you can tackle at your own pace, though we suggest setting aside time each week to finish the lessons over the course of six weeks. Whether you are taking this on as an individual or as a therapist, teacher, coach, or other leader who is guiding individuals or groups through this workbook as a curriculum, find a schedule that works, knowing that you or your clients can start, stop, and return to this workbook again and again to refresh your mindset and skills.

Getting Started

Although we define each new term and concept in this workbook so it can stand on its own, we do recommend reading the corresponding chapter of *More Than a Body* with the week's lessons beforehand to deepen your understanding and growth.

To complete the reflection exercises and challenges in this workbook, you will need a journal or notebook and something to write with. As you move forward with greater resilience, this record of your thoughts and impressions will be incredibly valuable to you for seeing how your relationship with your body has grown and evolved.

Before you jump into Chapter 1, be sure to first read the Introduction, then take the Self-objectification Score Quiz to get a baseline feel for your level of self-objectification.

Introduction

This workbook, like all our work, is oriented around what we believe is the missing piece in the larger body image and body positivity conversation: objectification. It's not just that girls and women don't feel beautiful, it's that they feel defined by their beauty. Objectification happens when people (primarily girls and women) are presented and viewed as objects or parts to be judged and consumed—not full, dynamic, thinking, feeling humans, but one-dimensional objects. When individuals are immersed in an objectifying environment, which our media and cultural landscape very much is, we learn to turn that degrading lens on ourselves. This is self-objectification. We learn to view and value our own bodies and selves as objects or parts to be judged and consumed by others.

To help you get a feel for how your thoughts and actions relating to your body might be affected by self-objectification, take this 15-question quiz to get your Self-objectification Score (SOS). Write down the number corresponding to each answer in your notebook. By recording your answers this way instead of circling them here, you can re-take this quiz again in the future. This quiz is important because it'll give you a baseline to start from that you'll use to reflect on and gauge changes in your feelings and behaviors going forward.

| Quiz | Self-objectification Score (SOS) Quiz |

A. When considering how you feel about your body, how much of your answer revolves around how you look (or how you think you look)?

1. Entirely revolves around how I look

2. Very much revolves around how I look

3. Somewhat revolves around how I look

4. A little revolves around how I look

5. None of it revolves around how I look

B. How often do you think about your appearance or how you look to others?

1. Constantly

2. Often

3. Sometimes

4. Very rarely

5. Never

C. How often do you change your plans or avoid certain people, activities, or events due to disliking how you look?

1. Constantly

2. Often

3. Sometimes

4. Very rarely

5. Never

D. How often do you weigh yourself, take your body measurements, or do other body checks to evaluate your size or shape?

1. Daily or more
2. Weekly or a few times per week
3. Monthly or every other week
4. Every few months
5. Only at the doctor's office or when unavoidable

E. How much do other people's thoughts or opinions about your body and appearance affect how you feel about your body?

1. They have a huge effect on how I feel. I seek out others' opinions often.
2. They have a pretty big effect on how I feel. I sometimes ask for others' opinions.
3. They sometimes do and sometimes don't have an effect on how I feel. I don't seek out or avoid others' opinions.
4. They have little effect on how I feel. I usually try to avoid others' opinions.
5. They have zero effect on how I feel. I avoid or ignore others' opinions.

F. How much time, effort, and money do you spend on your appearance on a daily/weekly/monthly basis, in your opinion?

1. A huge amount. I always work on maintaining or enhancing my appearance.

2. A pretty big amount. I frequently try to maintain or enhance my appearance.

3. A fair amount. I sometimes try to maintain or enhance my appearance.

4. A small amount. I rarely try to maintain or enhance my appearance.

5. A negligible amount. I make zero to minimal effort to maintain or enhance my appearance.

G. How body- and appearance-focused are the people you interact with the most, in your opinion?

1. Extremely. They constantly talk about their own and others' bodies.

2. Very. They frequently talk about their own and others' bodies.

3. Somewhat. They sometimes talk about their own and others' bodies.

4. Not very. They infrequently talk about their own or others' bodies.

5. Not at all. They never or very rare talk about their own or others' bodies.

H. How body- and appearance-focused are the environments and activities you spend the most time in and around outside your home? (i.e. gym, school, workplace, clubs, businesses)

1. Extremely. There is a constant focus on looking a certain way or fitting appearance ideals.

2. Very. There is a frequent focus on looking a certain way or fitting appearance ideals.

3. Somewhat. There is sometimes a focus on looking a certain way or fitting appearance ideals.

4. Rarely. There is not much of a focus on looking a certain way or fitting appearance ideals.

5. Not at all. There is no focus on looking a certain way or fitting appearance ideals.

I. How much time do you spend viewing, scrolling through, or otherwise engaging with media that reflects mostly idealized bodies and faces, in your opinion? (i.e. social media apps, videos, TV shows, movies, shopping websites, etc.)

1. A huge amount, very regularly

2. A pretty big amount, frequently

3. A fair amount, sometimes

4. A small amount, infrequently

5. Almost none, never or very rarely

J.   How much attention, positive or negative, was paid to your appearance by those closest to you growing up?

  1. A huge amount. There were constant comments about how I looked.

  2. A pretty big amount. There were frequent comments about how I looked.

  3. A fair amount. There were sometimes comments about my appearance.

  4. A small amount. There were rare comments about my appearance.

  5. Almost none. There were never or very rare comments about my appearance.

K.   Do you think it is possible for you to feel positively toward your body regardless of how it looks?

  1. Absolutely not

  2. Probably not

  3. Not sure

  4. Probably

  5. Definitely

L. How confident are you in your ability to make positive choices for your body, physically and mentally, including increasing or sustaining healthy behaviors and practicing skills to improve your body image?

1. Extremely unconfident. It feels impossible.

2. Somewhat unconfident. It feels unlikely.

3. Not sure. It feels neither way.

4. Somewhat confident. It feels likely.

5. Extremely confident. It feels highly likely.

M. How much do you think your weight, body mass index, body fat percentage, or dress size matters when it comes to how you understand your personal health and fitness?

1. A huge amount. I always rely on one or more of these measurements.

2. A pretty big amount. I usually rely on one or more of these measurements.

3. A fair amount. I sometimes rely on one or more of these measurements.

4. A small amount. I infrequently rely on one or more of these measurements.

5. None. I never rely on these measurements.

N. How much do you think your appearance matters to the people you are closest to?

1. A huge amount. Their thoughts and actions toward me revolve around how I look.

2. A pretty big amount. Their thoughts and actions toward me often change according to how I look.

3. A fair amount. Their thoughts and actions toward me sometimes change according to how I look.

4. A small amount. Their thoughts and actions toward me very rarely change according to how I look.

5. None. Their thoughts and actions toward me never change according to how I look.

O. If you saw a photo or video of yourself from today that you considered very unappealing or unattractive, how would you react?

1. It would ruin my whole day or week. I would immediately punish myself in some way and make drastic changes to my appearance or behavior.

2. It would have a major impact. I would avoid seeing people or going out until I fixed my appearance in some way or made plans to do so.

3. It would have somewhat of an impact. I would feel bad and might think about how to avoid looking that way in the future.

4. It would have a small impact. I might cringe at seeing it but probably move on to focus on other things.

5. It would have zero negative impact. I would laugh or ignore it if I even noticed it.

Calculate your Self-objectification Score (SOS) by adding up the numbers corresponding to each answer you selected. For example, if you answer "4" for Question A, you get 4 points. Total up the score for each answer and find your total in one of the four categories below.

15-29: 5-Alarm SOS

Based on your answers, it is very likely that you feel defined by your appearance most—if not all—of the time. Whether this fixation on looks started early in life or seeped in later, there's a good chance the people you care about and engage with the most also share this fixation on how people look instead of what they do or who they are. They might even comment often on how you look, whether positively or negatively. It is also very likely that your ideas of health and fitness are intertwined with ideas about sex appeal and current beauty ideals, defined by how you or others look instead of how you feel, what you do, and what internal medical tests might indicate.

30-44: High-Alert SOS

Your answers show that you likely feel fixated on how you look much of the time. Perhaps you regularly avoid seeing people or engaging in activities or events out of fear you don't look how you'd like to; or maybe you find yourself constantly sucking in, fixing your hair, scrolling through your own selfies, checking your makeup, or rearranging your position to appear more flattering. You are probably surrounded by others who do the same or place very high value on fitting beauty ideals. There is a high chance you judge your own health and fitness according to your weight or dress size and prioritize body goals over strength, endurance, or a clean bill of health at the doctor's office.

45-59: Stand-By SOS

Based on your answers, you likely feel somewhat positively or at least neutral toward your body on a typical day. You likely have bouts of feeling fixated on or ultra-conscious of how you appear, but that is not your constant state. While you may interact with people who judge themselves and others by their looks, you might find that their comments and opinions don't make or break how you feel, even if they do affect you sometimes. It is likely that those you are closest to are not looks-obsessed and value you for more than how you appear. You might be conscious of your weight or size and feel somewhat hung up on those measures when you think about your health and fitness, but you also consider other factors like your physical activity and medical tests.

60-75: All-Clear SOS

At any given moment, you probably feel comfortable in your body, whether peacefully neutral or full of gratitude and positivity. It is likely that you either grew up in an environment that placed very little emphasis on beauty or thinness or that you have worked to overcome an environment with extremely high emphasis on beauty or thinness. Whether by effort or luck, you are likely close to people who value you for who you are instead of how you look, and who are conscious of our society's harmful pressures regarding appearance. You have likely experienced periods or moments of feeling fixated on how you look, even today, but you know how to move forward in healthy ways despite those concerns. You might measure your health at least somewhat according to your weight or size, but you also value how you feel and how your habits and choices affect your experience inside your body.

Once you've read about where your Self-objectification Score falls, you might notice that some of it resonates with you and some of it doesn't—that's OK. This is meant only to give you a general baseline for how your body image might be impacted by objectification, or a fixation on appearance. You might notice we never asked if you love or hate how you look, or if you think you are beautiful or ugly. Instead, we are more concerned with how you relate to your body—are you an outside observer viewing and judging your body as an object, or are you an insider, embodied and judging your experience from within? In our research, we found that many people confuse "my body" with "how my body looks" and think of their bodies mostly from an outside perspective.

Being able to see and value yourself as more than a body to be looked at is key to developing a more positive body image, which will help you have the confidence to show up as you are and prioritize your first-person experience and fulfillment over how others perceive you. Living a life for others' viewing pleasure is not fully living, and you deserve to fully live.

Positive body image isn't believing your body looks good; it is knowing your body is good, regardless of how it looks. This workbook will help you internalize this knowledge and put it into practice until it becomes natural and instinctual.

1

Understanding Your Body Image

| Lesson 1.1 | The Sea of Objectification

> "You are more than a body, and you knew that once. It takes some serious work to remember, understand, and experience this truth that you are more—more than beautiful, more than parts in need of fixing, more than an object to be looked at and evaluated. Can you remember when you knew you were more?"
>
> —*More Than a Body*, p. 11-12

Though for some readers it might feel out of reach to be peacefully at home in your body and able to live comfortably without feeling anxious or ashamed about how you look, it helps to remember that it wasn't always this way. As little kids, we all lived free from hyper-awareness of our appearance. But unfortunately, those carefree days come to an end—for some earlier than others—due to all kinds of difficult and unavoidable experiences and circumstances.

To illustrate these shifts, we use the metaphor of a beach near a body of water, which we call the Sea of Objectification. Its deep waters surround us all, lapping up on the ground nearby, inviting us in with so many of our loved ones and peers. We went from feeling confidently at home hunched over a sandcastle on the beach or running along the shore as kids to eventually finding ourselves in the water. Here, the water represents our objectifying culture and all the many messages and reminders we receive about the importance of our appearance and sexual appeal.

Some of us are pushed into the water by the words and actions of others, whether loved ones innocently commenting on our growing bodies or strangers shouting vulgar comments on the street. Some of us are sucked into the sea by early exposure to pornography or sexual violence. Some of us dip our toes in as we become conscious of which bodies and faces get the most positive attention around us or in media. Whether you were invited or forced into this sea, slowly acclimating or suddenly immersed, this was your first taste of objectification, and your new awareness that people were judging your body (positively or negatively).

Venturing out into the water requires you to leave behind your whole embodied self on the beach, splitting your identity from someone who exists *to be* into someone who also exists *to be looked at*. Since most of the people in your life are already in those same waters, dealing with the same pressures, you eventually acclimate, and this environment becomes natural and invisible. Over time, you settle into what we think of as a "comfort zone life raft"—your everyday state of coping with objectification, or how you keep your body image afloat.

It's not very sturdy or all that comfortable, but it feels normal to you now and it usually keeps your head above water.

We want to draw your attention to the environment around you and all the factors that might have taught you to turn your focus to your body at the expense of your humanity.

Challenge for Now
Channeling a Childhood Beach Day

If possible, find a photo or video of yourself playing near water or wearing a swimsuit as a small child. If not, just think back on yourself as a kid—maybe you can even think of a specific day or experience by a pool or lake, playing in the sand or grass on a shore, accompanied by family or friends. Sit or lay in a comfortable position and read through the following prompts. Then, close your eyes for at least five uninterrupted minutes to visualize yourself as a child in this setting. Try to put yourself back into that moment.

- How did you look at that age? (Imagine each part of your face and body, including what you might have been wearing.)

- What were you doing to have fun at that moment? (Building a sandcastle, playing a game, rolling in the grass, interacting with friends or loved ones, etc.)

- What might it have felt like to be there without any thought of how you looked or who was watching?

When you open your eyes again, take a minute to consider what you felt by channeling your little self at that particular time. In your journal, write down a list of words that come to your mind about the experience. How would you describe that day and how you might have felt as a child in that setting? (e.g. carefree, joyful, excited)

Next, think about how you might feel today in the same setting or activity. If possible, think back on the last time you were swimming or hanging out near a body of water or doing a sunny day activity. In your journal, write down a list of words that come to your mind about the experience. How would you describe how you felt in that setting?

As you compare the two lists, how do they differ or overlap? Which words are the most appealing or aspirational to you? Circle or put a star next to the words you would like to experience more often as you build your body image resilience.

Lesson 1.2

Waves of Body Image Disruption

"Whether or not we are comfortable in our body image 'comfort zones,' every one of us will still face life experiences and societal pressures that push us out of our life rafts. These waves of body image disruption—things like facing unreal ideals in media, aging, pregnancy, injury, illness, bullying, criticism, self-comparison, abuse, and violence—will knock you over, throw you for a loop, and shake up your relationship with your own body...These waves are big and small and different for everyone, but what they have in common is that they cause you to feel self-doubt, shame, fear, or anxiety about your body, and they demand your attention and response."

—*More Than a Body,* p. 18

In the Sea of Objectification, you are constantly reminded of the importance of beauty and all the ways you are pressured to meet those standards. When those reminders are especially shocking or painful, they change the way you relate to your own body and the way you perceive yourself. We call these Waves of Body Image Disruption. They push you out of your everyday comfort zone and trigger your body shame and increased self-objectification.

When this happens, you are flipped out of your life raft and forced to react in order to keep your head above water and feel comfortable again. You might not even be conscious of the ways you react since these waves knock you around so regularly, and because your reactions might be instinctual at this point.

Challenge for Now
Describing Your Disruptions

Take a few quiet moments to consider the following questions, then reflect on them through writing in your journal.

- Describe the biggest Wave of Disruption you have faced in your life. What is an experience from your past that caused a major shift in how you felt about your body? What specifically happened that stirred up your body shame and caused you to feel especially fixated on your appearance?

- What exactly did you do to cope in that moment and afterward, for better or for worse?

- How did those choices or actions impact how you felt about your body, either in that moment or later? How did your reaction affect you positively or negatively?

- Describe the most recent Wave of Disruption you faced—big or small. What happened in the past several days or weeks that caused you to feel body shame or anxiety recently?

- What exactly did you do to cope in that moment and afterward, for better or for worse?

- How did those choices or actions impact how you felt about your body, either in that moment or later? How did your reaction affect you positively or negatively?

Lesson 1.3

Coping by Sinking, Hiding, or Fixing

"When our culture consistently portrays female bodies as parts served up on a platter to be used, evaluated, ogled, and cast aside, we can't blame [girls and women] for internalizing that darkness and coping in dark ways that sink them deeper into shame. When feeling beautiful and desirable remains the only solution we can imagine to the large-scale problem of body image concerns, of course we are left feeling worthless and deserving of pain. And when you don't know other ways to deal with the brutal realities of life in this dehumanizing environment, and you don't feel worthy or equipped to seek better options, allowing yourself to sink to the bottom might feel like a reasonable response and the only one you are capable of making."

—*More Than a Body,* p. 22

As you explored in the previous lesson, when you get pushed out of your body image comfort zone, you might have turned to a few different ways to cope with that shame and discomfort—some that might have helped a bit in the moment and some that might have hurt you even worse. In our research, we found that when faced with Waves of Body Image Disruption, people tend to respond by choosing two different paths.

We think of the first path as the worst path: Sinking Deeper into Shame. On this path, people consciously or subconsciously choose harmful coping mechanisms to numb or punish themselves or distract from the pain of hating their bodies. For example, substance use, including compulsive alcohol and illegal or prescription drug use, self-harm of all kinds, disordered eating, and anything else that provides immediate numbness or a different kind of pain (that often feels deserved because of perceived weakness, or feeling out of control, bad, or unworthy of love). The problem with this path is that, as the name suggests, it leaves people feeling even worse off than before. Once the high, distraction, numbness, or other pain fades, a person's feelings of disgust or discomfort with their body is often heightened.

Though the first path is the worst, the second path isn't very effective either. We call this Clinging to Your Comfort Zone, and it is likely familiar to everyone who has ever tried to cope with body shame. When you get knocked out of your life raft by a sudden trigger to your body shame or anxiety, it's only natural to try and get back to your normal body image state—even if it's not all that peaceful or positive. You end up clinging to your comfort zone by trying to hide your body or fix your body. Think of it like a fight-or-flight response, which is your body's automatic response to being scared or triggered. When triggered by a wave of disruption, some people try to fight their body by trying to fix its supposed "flaws," and some (even simultaneously) choose to hide by opting out of situations or activities where they think they'll be judged or where they don't look good enough to be seen.

Challenge for Now
Reflecting on Sinking, Hiding, or Fixing

Take a few quiet moments to consider the following questions, then reflect on them through writing in your journal.

- What, if any, choices have I made that caused me to sink deeper into shame after a body image disruption? How have I hurt, numbed, or punished myself when I felt bad about my body?

- What was the result of those choices, in the short term and the long term? How did those choices affect my body and how I felt about myself later?

- Has sinking deeper into shame brought lasting relief from my body shame?

- Does continuing to choose this path feel sustainable forever?

- If possible, discuss your answers to these questions with someone you trust like a family member, therapist, coach, or friend.

Next, please list any experiences, events, opportunities, or activities where you chose to hide due to not liking how you looked (or fearing how you would look).

- When have I opted out, stayed home, sat on the sidelines, not volunteered, not spoken up, or otherwise hid myself because I didn't look how I wanted to?

- What might I have missed out on by hiding?

Finally, consider how you have tried to "fix" your body after moments when you felt shame.

- What kind of fixes have I attempted to make to my appearance?

- Did those fixes work to improve the way I felt about myself at those times?

- Have I been able to fix my body enough to feel satisfied and comfortable to move forward?

- Has clinging to my comfort zone by hiding or fixing brought lasting relief from my body shame?

- Does continuing to choose this path feel sustainable forever?

| Lesson 1.4 | Enabling Disruptions: Rising with Resilience |

"[O]ur research-backed methods for personal body image transformation count on all of us experiencing the sea of objectification and its associated stressors and then using those degrading and painful experiences as motivators to tap into our own power to rise with resilience regardless of whether or not our environment changes to meet us there. Through our individual and then collective action, we can gradually create a better and safer environment not only for ourselves, but for everyone else who deserves to see and be seen as more than a body."

—*More Than a Body,* p. 30

Sinking deeper into shame and clinging to uncomfortable comfort zones might provide a temporary feeling of control or reprieve, but the problem is they don't provide lasting relief or meaningful change for you or anyone else. This creates a vicious cycle that most people live in forever, because even though it's exhausting, it feels normal and even deserved. Maybe you blame yourself for lacking self-control around food, not having enough discipline with punishing workouts, not putting in enough time, money, or effort on your hair or skin or clothes. You might feel like a failure when all the body positive messages telling you to LOVE your flaws don't really sink in, like you are the exception to the "all bodies are beautiful" idea because you are exceptionally unattractive or just so close to reaching the ideals that will help you feel worthy of confidence.

Our work provides a new path out of this endless cycle of comfort zone life raft > wave of disruption > sinking or hiding or fixing > back to comfort zone life raft. One fact about the Sea of Objectification is that the waves are a natural part of life in this environment—they will always keep coming because our profit-driven culture is obsessed with beauty, youth, and unreachable ideals—for everyone, but especially for women. And as long as your feelings about your body hinge on how you think you look at any given moment, those waves will keep knocking you out by overwhelming you with body shame or fixation on how you look.

Our goal for you is to look at those waves of disruption in a new way. Rather than being devastating triggers and reminders to cope in all your old unhelpful ways, they can be catalysts for lasting change in your life. The waves you face can become enabling disruptions, providing you with opportunities for growth, learning, and practice to choose a new path: Rising with Body Image Resilience.

 Challenge for Now
Becoming Conscious of Your Coping Style

In *More Than a Body*, we share a few examples of people who faced major disruptions to their body image and became stronger and more confident in their bodies—not in spite of their hard experiences, but because of what they learned through those experiences. Have you ever experienced one of these enabling disruptions—or a painful experience that eventually helped you grow or learn something you wouldn't have learned otherwise? In your journal, reflect on the following questions:

- What have I gained from painful disruptions to my body image? How have I grown, learned, gained new perspective, new skills or resources, or increased my compassion for myself or others by facing difficult experiences with my body?

- In what ways have I seen other people in my life grow or improve their lives in response to trials or difficulties?

- What motivates me to choose the third path of rising with resilience instead of sinking into shame or clinging to my comfort zone?

- How might building my body image resilience help me or those I care about in the future?

Summary

Chapter 1
Understanding Your Body Image

Through a metaphor of your carefree child self on the beach and making your way into the Sea of Objectification that surrounds us, you have gained a new way of thinking about your body image and what has shaped it into the way you feel about your body today. Being able to recognize your uncomfortable body image comfort zone and how you typically cope with waves of body image disruption is crucial.

Now, you'll be able to notice when something triggers your body shame or fixation on appearance and give it a name: a Wave of Body Image Disruption. Now, you'll be able to stop and consider your reaction to that wave that might have felt automatic before. You'll be able to notice if you are tempted to sink into shame with harmful coping mechanisms, or cling to your comfort zone by hiding or fixing your body. Now, you know how fleeting, disappointing, and ineffective those paths are for you. Now, you have the chance to choose a new path by letting those waves propel you forward to rise with body image resilience.

The goal of this workbook is to help you build your body image resilience muscle, or the ability to respond to moments of body shame and self-objectification in ways that reconnect you with your body as your home instead of turning you against yourself. Thankfully, as you build this muscle, the waves of body image disruption stop being so disruptive and your conscious responses to them become easier with practice.

The rest of this workbook will focus on the skills, tools, and strengths you'll need to choose this third path and rise with body image resilience every time you confront a body image disruption. You'll notice that some of these skills will feel easy and innate to you, while others will require a little more practice. All of them will help you come home to your body and better connect to who you really are and what you are capable of.

Challenge for Later
Taking Inspiration from Kids

If you have the opportunity to spend any time around young children, take some time in the coming days to simply observe them as they play alone or interact with others. What does it look like for a kid to navigate their world without self-consciousness? How can you learn from their example? What could your life look like with less body monitoring or anxiety?

Challenge for Later
Digging into Resilience

Do you know someone who has shown resilience or who has overcome great difficulty in some aspect of their life? If possible and where appropriate, ask them if they would be willing to talk to you about the challenges they have faced and how they were able to overcome them, or grow and learn as a result of them. As you listen to their story, find out what innate skills or traits they used to thrive in difficult moments. What skills or traits did they develop or gain access to as a result of the challenges they experienced? What advice do they have for you or others who experience tough circumstances or waves of disruption?

2

Critiquing and Creating Your Body Image Environment

Lesson 2.1   ## Media that Shaped You

"Television, movies, magazines, video games, and social media are some of the most prevalent—and inescapable—sources of messaging that objectifies women and girls, and their reach begins in childhood. Slowly but surely, we piece together each new message we receive to form our very first body image maps, where X marks the spot at the destination of 'feel beautiful.' These are the maps we will use to understand and navigate the treacherous waters of objectification for years to come. Formed in our minds but as tangible as a handheld document, our body image maps shift and evolve over time based on changing currents of beauty ideals and the discovery of new routes toward body confidence and desirability."

—*More Than a Body,* p. 41

Regardless of whether you grew up with only traditional media like TV, movies, and magazines or you had access to social media and individual content creators, the media you consumed helped set the standard for how people should look and who is most valuable. These ideals, formed by popular media that represents a distorted view of reality, create a sort of body image map that guides how you perceive and treat your body, including the goals or "destinations" to which you aspire.

In TV and movies, the male characters almost always outnumber the female ones, and they get to show up in a variety of bodies and be defined by more than how they appear. When it comes to age, media features older men 10 times more frequently than older women. Girls and women, on the other hand, are too often sexualized and confined to very narrow definitions of beauty in order to be featured at all. The sexism in kids' movies is especially blatant, with male characters generally getting twice as much speaking time as female characters, who also generally fit the same mold: thin-yet-curvaceous bodies, big eyes and lips, tiny noses and chins, and often a sidekick or love interest instead of a lead or protagonist.

These ideas of what defines femininity are then cemented in our collective consciousness for generations. It is no wonder that so many people's body image maps lead to similar destinations or "body goals" that reflect exactly what is most popular and prized in the media we consume.

Challenge for Now
Reflecting on Your Media Memories

In *More Than a Body*, Lindsay and Lexie reference the TV show "Saved by the Bell" and a specific episode about Zack's prom date as an example of something that informed their ideas of which bodies were acceptable and which were not. Using your journal, reflect on the media messages that shaped how you perceived your body and others' growing up.

- What TV shows, movies, magazines, content creators, celebrities, or other media had the most impact on how you thought about bodies and appearance when you were young? Be specific about particular images, episodes, characters, or messages that stuck in your mind to form your opinions about how you or others should look.

- What messages did you learn from those examples?

- How would you describe the average character, actress, or influencer in those media examples that most impacted you? How did they look in terms of size, shape, age, hair texture, color and length, complexion, skin tone, etc.?

- How did you believe you compared to the "norm" you saw in media? What, if anything, did you think you needed to change about your appearance in order to meet those standards of normal or acceptable set by media?

Lesson 2.2

Immersed in Objectification from Head to Toe

"From head to toe, we have been trained to understand every part of our bodies as a potential problem to be solved, regardless of how common, natural, and unproblematic each 'problem area' really is. None of those supposed flaws would be of concern if we valued those parts of our bodies for the function they serve and how we experience them from inside ourselves. All of those supposed flaws and the pressure we feel to fix them are purely the result of evaluating our bodies (and being evaluated) based on how we appear."

—*More Than a Body,* p. 69

In our profit-driven media world, where women control trillions of dollars in worldwide spending and are primarily in control of the dollars in most U.S. households, it isn't surprising that women are targeted with unreachable beauty ideals. From birth, girls are taught to find value in being decorative, with each part of their bodies representing a flaw to be fixed or a part to be flaunted to gain validation and confidence.

Since the moment you dipped your toes into the Sea of Objectification, you may have learned to see yourself through

a critical, appearance-focused perspective. You may be starting to realize that seeing your body as a long checklist of
problem areas is exhausting, expensive, dehumanizing and
not very fulfilling. It is time to work on shifting your attention
from questioning your body to questioning how you have
been trained to see your body and why.

Challenge for Now
Examining Your "Problem Areas"

In your journal or on a sheet of paper, draw a small outline of
your body (even a stick figure will do), leaving plenty of space
around the figure for writing. Starting at the top of your head
and moving down to your toes, draw a line or arrow to each
visible part of your body that you have learned to consider a
"flaw" in your appearance. Next to the line or arrow, label
that particular "problem area" using the words you have associated with each "flaw." For example, you might have an arrow
pointing to your eyelashes that says "too short/sparse/light" or
an arrow to your thighs that says "cellulite," etc. List as many
as you feel are relevant to the way you have perceived yourself throughout your life.

Now, using another color or setting this new addition apart
in parentheses or brackets, list any "solutions" you have been
sold (whether you literally purchased a product or service or
figuratively bought into the idea that it could solve your
"problem area"). For example, if you labeled "cellulite" on
your legs, write "[liposuction, firming cream, shapewear, X
influencer's squat regimen]" or whatever solutions you've
been sold for that particular issue.

As you look over the entire list of supposed problems and solutions, reflect in writing on the following prompts:

- Who or what decided that those physical characteristics should be diagnosed as "problems," and who (literally or figuratively) benefits from you buying into the "solutions?"

- Are those same characteristics or features labeled as flaws also considered to be problems when they are on people of the other sex? Are the same solutions sold to people of the other sex? (For example, "short, sparse eyelashes" would not be considered a flaw on a man.)

- Have these supposed "flaws" always been considered problems throughout time, or can you think of a time in history or even in your life when they wouldn't have been thought of as less than ideal? (For example, the standards around the color and shape of teeth have changed drastically in the past decade, and forehead wrinkles were hardly questioned before Botox became normalized.)

- Would you consider each of these characteristics as "problem areas" if they were on your child or someone you love unconditionally?

- Is it possible the real problem with each of these parts is your perception of them, or the way you've been taught to dislike them?

Lesson 2.3

The Lens of
Media Literacy

"The most empowering part of learning to be more media savvy is finding that this is an active—not passive—new way of being. The ability to be media literate and effectively deconstruct your body image map isn't just about knowing what to avoid and how outside messages impact you. It is also about realizing you have the power and opportunity to construct a new understanding of your body and the world you inhabit and experience with your body. You have the power to replace your old, misleading body image map with a new set of skills and resources that can guide you toward resilience."

—*More Than a Body*, p. 70

Media literacy is the ability to critically understand the way media is created to influence your perceptions. It requires being able to interrogate the choices and messages made by companies and individuals to determine what is true and what is false; what preys on your insecurities and attempts to manipulate your reality versus what serves you. The power to be media literate will allow you to call out and avoid the messages that cause you to feel self-conscious and ashamed, while helping you to amplify and create content that empowers you and others to be more than a body.

The first step to being more media literate is to question everything to determine how the media you consume impacts your thoughts and actions. The answers you find give you the opportunity to act: to avoid and speak out against the messages that distort your perception of yourself or others, to create and amplify content that represents the reality you already see or want to see, and to teach others how to be careful and conscious of how media impacts them and their communities.

Challenge for Now
Questioning Everything

Spend 30 minutes with your go-to form of entertainment media. If that is scrolling through your favorite social media apps while streaming a show in the background, do it! If that is watching a movie, surfing YouTube, or turning on a channel you love, watch it. If you prefer to listen to music or a podcast or flip through a magazine, go for it. When the 30 minutes are up, answer the following questions in your journal:

- Do I feel better or worse about myself when I see, hear or read this? Would the people in my life feel better or worse about themselves after consuming this?

- Does it spark body anxiety or feelings of shame?

- Does it cause me to engage in self-comparison?

- Who profits from me believing these messages? Who is advertising here? (Look for ads, sponsors or sponsored content, commercials, and product placement, and you'll see who is paying the bills for the media you consume, or who is getting paid when you see it.)

- Does this message seek to profit from my insecurities by selling solutions to fix my "flaws"?

- What kind of audience is this message trying to target?

- Am I being asked to value the people in this content for their talents, words, personality, or character, or their appearance or sexual appeal?

- Does it encourage me to fixate on my own or others' appearances?

- Does it promote or reinforce distorted ideals of what bodies and faces should look like—either through digital manipulation, filters, featuring only one body type or "look," or criticizing certain looks?

If the content you're seeing mostly or always reflects certain body or beauty ideals or keeps you focused on how others perceive you, you might want to train your social media algorithms to feed you content that exposes you to a more diverse array of people, ideas, and messages. Consider the following:

- Who or what am I going to mute, unfollow, or click "not relevant to me" or "I don't want to see this" where possible?

- What kinds of creators or messages am I going to seek out and interact with more often?

- How can I remember to be more conscious and critical while I'm watching or scrolling through mediated content? (Consider checking in with yourself by asking something like: How am I feeling while I'm engaging with this content? Does this content trigger my shame, self-objectification, self-comparison, or loneliness?)

| Lesson 2.4 |

Actively Engaging as Consumers and Creators

"You have the opportunity to participate in shaping what comes into your home and social media feeds, and you have the right to speak up when something is causing harm. Be brave in calling out messages that are hurtful and degrading. Hold media makers accountable for their content and its impact on consumers. Raise warning flags for passersby that these ideals are unsafe and unreachable and that the routes toward them are filled with danger. You might discover you have insights people are eager to hear and amplify."

—*More Than a Body,* p. 97

You are more than a body. Your appearance doesn't define your worth. That's a hard message to believe and act upon when you've grown up subtly hearing the opposite. You can take the pain of living in a sexist, objectifying, dehumanizing world and use it to not only be more but push for more and better for everyone. To make change, to speak louder, to act with more compassion, to advocate for those who are silenced or harmed, to take up more space, and to stand up for what you believe in.

Thanks to social media, you have more power than ever before to create the content and amplify the messages you want to see, make your voice heard, and connect with others who are like-minded. When we (Lexie and Lindsay) began our body image research many years ago, we established a blog and a Facebook page, followed by an Instagram page a few years later. Sharing our work and our insights in reader-friendly bites online changed our lives and gave us a platform to connect with thousands of people who needed to hear that they are more than a body. Activism happens offline, too, through community groups and events, volunteering, education and research, teaching, political campaigns, protests and petitions, and supporting businesses and people who align with you and your beliefs. Do not underestimate the power you have to create a kinder, more inclusive body image environment in your circles of influence.

Challenge for Now
Representing Reality

Everyone who has a presence online, particularly through social media, has an opportunity to represent reality, create and amplify positive content, and disrupt the steady flow of images and messages that reinforce the same old beauty- and body-centric messages, even in small ways. Open the platform you use most often, then review your profile page and the content you have created and shared (photos/videos, captions, memes, posts, etc.). Take some time to scroll through your content and then, using your journal, reflect on the following questions:

- How do I feel about how I have chosen to represent myself and/or my family here?

- Have I changed how I show up on this platform since I started posting? If so, in what ways?

- Who is my target audience? (Is there anyone in particular I want to see my posts?)

- What are my goals with posting and sharing content on this platform? (Sharing my life with friends, family, or others; connecting with others; attracting romantic partners; receiving validation from others; selling products or increasing engagement for sponsorship deals; promoting my views and beliefs, etc.)

- How body- and beauty-centric is the content I share?

- Do I use filters or edit my photos and videos to change my appearance or others? If so, why?

- Is this profile an accurate, realistic representation of me? Why or why not?

- Is there anything I feel like I could change about what I share online to better reflect who I am and what I value in myself or others?

Challenge for Now

Creating and Amplifying Positive Media

There are countless ways we as individuals can create and amplify positive messages and push for change from industries, companies, influencers, and media makers who have default-ed to objectification or excluding women and marginalized people. Consider the influence of those of us who have social media profiles, jobs in media or marketing or other influential industries that reach large audiences, talents and skills in content creation, dollars to spend in thoughtful ways, dollars to withhold from careless people and companies, and so many more ways to leverage small amounts of power into larger momentum and change.

Using the following list as a starting point, circle or write down each action item you are willing to try and add any others you would like to incorporate to create and amplify positive change starting with media in your life, your community, or beyond.

- Create and amplify social media content that features diversity in all its forms—race, ethnicity, gender, disability, body diversity, etc.

- Amplify, comment, share, and follow accounts that promote body diversity.

- Unfollow accounts that objectify women or profit from selling unreal ideals.

- If you are a student or considering going back to school, take classes that teach media skills, whether that is graphic design, creative writing, video production and editing, script writing, media literacy, journalism, strategic communication or public relations, marketing and advertising, etc.

- If you work in marketing or advertising, push back against messages that diagnose "flaws" in appearance or mock or vilify diverse bodies. Make suggestions for how your company or your clients might represent people with more inclusivity and compassion.

- Ensure your company's website, social media pages, advertising messages, or other public-facing media is inclusive in who is represented and featured.

- Look at who the decision-makers and leadership are for the companies you work for and the businesses you support, and if they exclude women, people of color, or other groups you value, consider having a conversation with management or otherwise making your concern about a lack of inclusivity known, and where possible, take your business elsewhere.

- If you are a teacher at any level, include media literacy lessons in your curriculum to help your students understand the power and influence of media in their lives and how they can be conscious creators.

- Volunteer to support nonprofits or groups that advocate for change as it relates to media, body image, objectification, or any subject you wish to amplify and support.

- What other action items can you think of to create and amplify positive media in your sphere of influence?

Summary

Chapter 2
Critiquing and Creating Your Body Image Environment

As you have learned throughout this chapter, building your body image resilience requires you to take a closer look at the media you consume to determine what has shaped and distorted your ideas about your "problem areas" and their supposed solutions. As you use your media literacy lens to consider what ideals and messages you have spent too much time, money, and energy pursuing, you have the opportunity to chart a new course. You can choose to be more mindful of the media you consume and how often you consume it, realizing that social media can work as self-help or self-harm depending on how you use it. You can use your social media presence and your media skills to disrupt the steady flow of idealized bodies, faces, and lives and reflect a more representative and inclusive reality.

As you go forward, the following challenges can help you build more skills for creating and critiquing your media environment.

Challenge for Later
Intermittent Media Fasting

Occasionally (or intermittently) taking a break from media helps you recognize how often you turn to media to fill your time and the reasons you might turn to it. When you choose to regularly step back from media, you give yourself a chance to get re-sensitized to the messages that might be sparking your body anxiety or otherwise normalizing harmful ideas, and also get reacquainted with your own thoughts, how you spend your time, whether you are actually enjoying yourself or just endlessly scrolling and feeling worse afterward.

For this challenge, choose at least one day (but ideally three to five days) to do a media fast. From the moment you wake up, avoid as much media as humanly possible. Do your best not to view or listen to any TV, movies, or podcasts, or use any social media. It is going to be difficult, and you will surely still consume some media without trying to, but try to prioritize cutting out any content about bodies (which even podcast ads regularly focus on).

Once your fast is complete, record your thoughts about what you experienced in your journal by reflecting on the following questions:

- Were you surprised by how often you considered turning to social media, or how mindlessly you turned on that TV or podcast as background noise or an escape? What feelings were you experiencing when you automatically turned to media? (Anxiety, boredom, etc.)

- What did you choose to do with your time and attention instead of engaging with media?

- How did it feel to spend more time with your own thoughts or with more attention to expend elsewhere?

- Less media consumption for one or two days might not feel like much, but that short period of time can give you cues about how and why you turn to media and how you can make your life better through more conscious choices. Do you feel like this intermittent media fast had a positive effect on you? If so, how?

- Do you plan to try out a media fast again, or on a particular schedule? Are there any other ways you would like to change your media use due to this experience?

Challenge for Later
Reconsidering Social Media

If you are a social media user (particularly Instagram, TikTok, Facebook, X/Twitter, or other interactive platform with a visual focus), take on this challenge for yourself. If you aren't a social media user, ask a young person in your life (ideally 13+) who is active on social media to have a conversation with you about the best and worst parts of using these platforms. For parents or caretakers, this conversation would also be great for younger kids who are interested in using social media for the first time.

Using your journal, start with creating a "pros" list of all the benefits of social media by considering for yourself or asking the other person what they like about social media or think they'd like about using it. A potential list of upsides might be:

Pros:

- I can interact with my friends online and meet new people.

- I can participate in fun and entertaining communities where people share their talents, hobbies, insights, and humor.

- I am exposed to interesting content and important ideas and people I might not see otherwise, like news, body positivity, activism, experts, and entertainers.

- I can express myself through posting pictures, videos, insights, and captions.

Next, ask yourself or the other person to consider what the "cons" of using social media might be, or what you/they don't like or might not like about using social media. What could you see or be exposed to that could be harmful or hurtful? What aspects of engaging with social media could affect you negatively? (If you are a caretaker having this conversation with a child or teen, be honest with them about what you have experienced and what you have learned about social media use). You might consider including potential cons or downsides like those below.

Cons:

- I might feel lonelier. Social media can be isolating and leads to a fear of missing out. (Many users report feeling more alone and isolated.)

- I might be more likely to experience depression and anxiety. (The more time spent on social media, the worse these feelings can get.)

- I might be more likely to feel bad about my body because I will be more conscious of how I look after seeing so many idealized, edited photos, ads, and highlight reels.

- I will be more likely to be exposed to harmful messages that will negatively impact me, like pornography, self-harm, pro-eating disorder messaging, misleading advertising, etc.

Once your pros and cons lists are complete, take some time to consider what kinds of boundaries you might set for yourself (or in partnership with a young person if you are their caretaker) around social media use. You might find that your cons far outweigh your pros and consider deleting or stepping back from social media. You might want to implement time limits, privacy settings, criteria to determine who you follow and interact with, or other examples like those found on p. 96 of *More Than a Body*.

3

Moving From Self-Objectification to Self-Care

The Loneliness of Self-Comparison

"Beauty isn't a limited resource in our world. Neither is love, attraction, validation, peace, intelligence, or happiness. But a world with narrow and highly prized ideals about bodies divides us into hierarchies of who looks right and who doesn't, and then ties our hopes for achieving all of those good things to our ability to climb the hierarchy. This pits us against our own bodies and each other in a constant state of comparison—whether to our past selves, our future body goals, or the woman in the office down the hall. This limiting, demeaning, divisive way of being causes us to become the watcher and the watched, the seer and the seen. We watch ourselves and compare the person we see to everyone else around us."

—*More Than a Body*, p. 122

A whole body of research over decades has found that women who compare themselves to others have greater body anxiety and body dissatisfaction. When you harshly judge yourself, your self-consciousness is magnified, and this preoccupation with your looks leads you to feel isolated and competitive. The very act of self-comparison, even when it's a favorable comparison (meaning we feel better than the other person), not only causes our body image to plummet, but causes us to feel divided, alone, antagonistic, and distanced from other women—both in real life and online. It's time to consider how this has impacted your relationship with your own body and with other people.

Challenge for Now
Revisiting Relationships

Have you missed out on fulfilling relationships with people in your life because you were stuck in a rut of self-comparison? Using your journal, reflect on the following questions:

- When have I avoided getting to know people because of my judgments about their looks? Who might I have ignored or discounted because I considered them too beautiful, too ugly, too fat, too thin, too sexy, too looks-obsessed, too unfashionable, or otherwise too different from me or too much competition for me?

- When have my judgments about someone based on their looks been proven wrong? Who has surprised me or positively influenced my life despite what I initially thought of them based on surface-level judgments?

- What kinds of bonds with other people do I want in my life? Am I open to breaking down my biases in order to learn from others, create more friendships, or build my community?

- How could I be more conscious of my limiting judgments going forward to better bond with and feel unified with other people, including those I might initially feel intimidated by or better than?

| Lesson 3.2 |

The Comfort of Self-Compassion

"Self-compassion means having your own back—accepting yourself and your past choices unconditionally. This way of being can help you survive disappointments, disruptions, less-than-ideal responses to those disruptions, and deflated comfort-zone life rafts. It won't prevent the difficulties that we all face, but it can help you get through them."

—*More Than a Body*, p. 142

When you reflect on the time you have spent isolated from your full, embodied self and those you care about in the Sea of Objectification, feelings of regret or resentment might bubble up to the surface. But if you are dedicated to letting go of the self-hate you have grown so accustomed to, you can't continue to punish yourself for who you are and how you have learned to cope.

As you practice self-compassion, you can develop the capacity to forgive yourself for the time, energy, and money you have spent in fruitless pursuits of unattainable beauty and body ideals. You can recognize the objectifying conditions you have grown up in and congratulate yourself for how hard you have tried to survive instead of berating yourself for those choices. Committing to a compassionate approach to yourself, you can choose to start reacting in more healthful and helpful ways because you respect and care about yourself—not because you hate yourself and deserve punishment.

Challenge for Now
Healing Through Your Higher Self

Find a space to be alone and lay down or sit in a position that is most comfortable for you. Shut your eyes and take several deep breaths in and out. Think back to a time, long ago or currently, when you coped with painful feelings toward your body in a way that didn't serve you. Perhaps you found yourself sinking deeper into shame through self-harm, a substance use disorder or addiction, disordered eating, or risky sexual behavior. Perhaps you chose to cling to your comfort zone through hiding and missing out on events and activities or trying to "fix" it through crash diets, restrictive shapewear, cosmetic procedures, or excessive beauty work. Rather than berating yourself for sinking deeper into shame or hiding and fixing so much of your life away, it's time to practice self-compassion.

Envision your "higher self" sitting directly in front of you. Their presence is warm and inviting. This person looks like you, but they exist beyond the physical realm—before this moment, during this moment, and after this moment, infinitely. They truly know you and feel great concern and compassion for you. They love all of you, including your body, and they are not in any way ashamed of you or for you. They intimately know everything you have gone through and everything you will go through in your life. They are proud of all you have accomplished and how you have handled your challenges, even the ones you know you struggled through and could have responded to differently.

As your higher self sits in front of you, they speak powerfully and lovingly to you. Either write in your journal or repeat aloud the following statements three times:

[Your name], I love you.

You are good.

I know you have felt real pain and shame.

I am so sorry for all you have dealt with.

I am so sorry for the way others have hurt you
   and used you.

You are not alone in your struggles.

You are normal and human.

You are not wrong for reacting the way you did to your
   feelings of pain and shame.

I forgive you for the ways you coped that didn't really
   help, and sometimes made things worse.

I forgive you for the negative beliefs and feelings you
   have toward your body and yourself.

You are worthy of love exactly as you are.

Your experiences have made you stronger, more
   knowledgeable, more compassionate, and better
   prepared to face future challenges.

This body has always been and will always be your home.

Thank you for choosing to come back home to this body
   even when it is difficult.

[Your name], I love you.

Next, sit in silence for a few more minutes as you envision what more your higher self might have to share with you. What else do they need you to know about your purpose, your power, your potential? What more do they want you to remember about who you really are?

After you've finished this visualization, write down the thoughts and takeaways that impressed you the most.

| Lesson 3.3 | ## Reaching Out

> "So many of us feel compelled to suffer alone out of shame, but our silence holds shame in power. When dark feelings arise from self-comparison or even from self-reflection, you can use them as an opportunity to open up to trusted people—online, in real life, through a call or a letter or a text, or even in an anonymous discussion forum. Signal to others that you could use some help or solidarity."
>
> *—More Than a Body*, p. 147

Self-objectification and self-comparison serve to isolate you from others—turning you inward, whether you are self-obsessed or self-loathing (or both). This often leads to shallow, unfulfilling relationships because you can't be vulnerable or secure enough with yourself to deeply connect with others. When you withhold your honest experiences and beliefs about yourself, whether out of embarrassment, shame, or fear of judgment or rejection, you are missing an opportunity to connect with others who can empathize or help.

While silence holds shame in power, sharing your painful experiences with others you trust helps lighten the burden, even if you've been carrying it your whole life and feel like you've got it under control. By reaching out instead of turning inward, you can create a powerful network of support for more than just yourself. Signal to someone you trust that you need a confidant and if possible, make it known that you can be one, too, by being willing to lend help to others in their own challenges. Your ability to be vulnerable and honest will help you unite with those who need it and move from lonely isolation to a community of support. No one needs or deserves to navigate the dark waters of objectification alone.

Challenge for Now
Sharing Your Burdens

It is likely you have faced a body image disruption that you quickly buried and tried to forget, never to speak of again or to process with a trusted confidant. When those painful or shameful moments stay buried in your psyche, they can take on outsized power that casts a shadow on your self-talk and your future experiences.

Reflect on a particular experience in or about your body that you could benefit from sharing with a trusted resource like a loved one, friend, coach, or therapist. Reach out to your selected confidant with a variation of the following examples:

- Text or call a loved one: "I was wondering if we could find some time to talk. I am working on healing my body image and have an experience I want to talk through with you. Even if you don't have any answers for me, just having a hug from you will help."

- Schedule a therapy or counseling session and ask to work through the specific experience.

- Email or text a trusted teacher, coach, or mentor: "Do you have a few minutes to talk this week? I am working on healing my body image and had an experience I'd like to talk through with you. I really trust you and I'd like your advice on next steps for dealing with it in a healthy way."

- Join a private online forum with others who are willing to listen and support you. Share the details of your experience you feel comfortable with or ask if someone you trust would be willing to private message you to talk about what you experienced and offer advice or empathy.

- If a conversation would be difficult, write a letter or email to your loved one to share your experience and your feelings around it. Let them know you needed to get the burden off your shoulders and ask them for what might be helpful, whether it is a hug, advice, sympathy, or simply a witness to what you faced.

If you don't get the support you feel you need, or you realize that you need more help and support than you had previously considered, please reach out to a therapist or even an emergency hotline for additional care. Some burdens require more attention and processing, and there is no shame in reaching out to a professional who is willing and prepared to help.

| Lesson 3.4 |

Reconnecting with Yourself

"I recognized that experiences in my own childhood shaped my body image in negative ways and drew me into the waters of objectification. But even knowing this, I didn't directly confront my own 'inner child' until I started therapy on my own. It melted. My. Heart...My mind immediately went to a picture of me as a five-year-old on Easter, sitting on a brown striped couch, smiling sweetly with a white bunny cradled in my arms. I am wearing baggy yellow pleated pants and a pink pastel sweatshirt zipped up to my chin. My blond hair is pulled into a ponytail on top of my head and my bangs and some short side hair are curled and fluffed up (the '90s go-to look for little girls). I absolutely love this picture of me. I can't even believe it's me because I'm so little and adorable, yet it is so totally me."

—*More Than a Body*, p. 151-152

While you may not remember all the details of your childhood, your experiences (the happy and the difficult) and what you learned from those things impact you in adulthood. The therapeutic practice of "inner child" work taps into the subconscious beliefs you have carried around since you were young and helps you unpack how those beliefs impact your feelings and choices. Reconnecting with your inner child, who we refer to as "Little You," will help you understand and work through the experiences that impacted you negatively so you can heal your relationship with your body and yourself.

Challenge for Now
A Letter for Little You

Find a photo or video of yourself from your childhood, ideally before or right around puberty or the time you remember feeling the first stings of body shame, self-objectification, or judgment from others. Look carefully at that photo or video, and if none are accessible, just take a moment to lovingly connect to and recall a moment as your little self in your mind as you think through some guiding questions. Close your eyes and imagine your Little You as you answer them. Imagine you are in the room together. How would it feel most natural to show your affection to the little you? You might imagine putting your arm around them, sitting them on your lap, holding their hand, or wrapping them in a hug.

Using your journal, write a letter to your Little You, like the one Lindsay shared in *More Than a Body* (p. 153). Alternatively, you could record a voice note or memo on your phone or computer if speaking feels more powerful to you than writing. Write or speak directly to Little You, as if they are sitting beside you today.

What do you want your Little You to know about themself and the coming waves of body image disruption in their life? What would you tell them about their worth, power, soul, body? Tell them how you feel about them and what truths you want them to keep throughout their life.

Remind your Little You that their experiences and difficulties will be instrumental in teaching and shaping them into their future self, and that their life has meaning. Which of your life experiences, talents, strengths, or contributions would you highlight as being especially meaningful?

Let Little You know that more difficulties will come, but then expresses unwavering confidence that they will face them with strength and resilience.

Keep this letter or voice note and revisit it whenever you start to feel burdened by body shame or disconnected from your body. Remember that little, perfect, lovable person you're imagining is still you. The same you. Older, bigger, wiser, yes. But absolutely you, and exactly as worthy of love now as you were then.

As you go forward, revisit the same old photo, video, or mental image of your younger self. Set that photo as your phone's wallpaper, carry the physical photo with you, or keep it somewhere you'll see it regularly. During the day, remind yourself that little person is still you—their body is still your body, their face is still your face, and let that sense of reconnection heal and inform how you see yourself.

Summary

Chapter 3

Moving From Self-Objectification to Self-Care

You can be more than a body, utilizing your pain to grow instead of shrink. You can use the inevitable self-objectification that tempts you to split from your whole self as an opportunity to make a new choice that serves you. Instead of punishing and isolating yourself when your body shame is triggered, you can practice self-compassion toward your past ways of coping, as well as the future inevitable mistakes you will make from a place of shame and self-objectification.

If you tend to default to self-comparison or making snap judgments of others based on how they look or dress, you can recognize the loneliness and missed opportunities that come from pitting yourself against others. You can practice reconnecting with others through honesty and vulnerability instead of isolation and shame and seek the help you deserve while offering your own support to others. You can reintroduce yourself to that Little You whom you may not have connected with in years, healing parts of you that have desperately needed validation and love.

To further develop your skills for rising with resilience in the face of self-objectification, complete the following challenges:

Challenge for Later
Getting Back Inside Your Body

When you are facing the pain of body anxiety or shame, it is easy to be in your head, hypothesizing about worst-case scenarios and playing out fears—not living in concrete reality. When your anxiety arises or you start to self-objectify by slipping outside of yourself to monitor your appearance, it is time to shift back inside your own body. In the next few days, when you feel yourself slipping into a cloud of anxiety about how you appear, call yourself back home. Try the following practice, modified for your own abilities and circumstances:

- First, relax your stomach as you start taking deep breaths, in and out. Too many of us are used to sucking in our stomachs and holding our abs tight throughout the day to hide our bellies. This prevents good, oxygen-rich blood from reaching the bottom of your lungs and circulating throughout your whole body.

- Breathe in through your nose, feeling your lungs fill with air. Breathe out through your mouth slowly. On the in-breath, think, "this is your home." On the out-breath, think, "welcome home." Let these words remind you that your body has always been and will always be your own, your home. Thank your lungs for allowing you to breathe.

- Look around and take in everything you can see. Look out as far as your eyes can see. Look closely at every detail, every color, every pattern, every texture, every shape, the lightness and darkness. Thank your eyes for what you can see.

- Listen to the sounds going on around you. Identify the quietest sounds you can hear, as well as the loudest. Listen for patterns in the sounds, for expected and unexpected sounds. Thank your ears for what you can hear.

- Touch your heart, holding your palm to your chest. If you're in public and not comfortable doing so, simply touch your leg, other hand or arm, or whatever feels comfortable. Thank your body for being your home and for growing and evolving with you since you were born. Feel the love and power emanating from your hand into your body. Repeat the words you have chosen to call yourself back into your body: This is your home. Welcome home.

- From your toes to your scalp, let a wave of gratitude wash over you as you breathe thanks into each part of your body. Release any tension you feel. Roll your shoulders and unclench your jaw. Repeat the words you have chosen to call yourself back home.

Note: For those with chronic illnesses, injuries, or disabilities, please know you don't need to ignore your pain or feel gratitude toward it. It is important to acknowledge the pain, disappointment, and difficulties we face in our bodies. As you do, where possible, try to hold your pain in balance with all your body's other feelings and functions, rather than letting it overpower your whole experience of your body.

Challenge for Later
Beauty Work Inventory

It is important to consider all the ways you have bought into beauty expectations just to feel like "yourself" or present the best possible version of "you." When it comes to grooming choices, it is up to each of us to figure out what is oppressive and what is creative self-expression or simply personal preference. When are you coping with shame by trying to hide or fix your "flaws"? When are you having fun using fashion and makeup as creative self-expression? Taking inventory of your beauty-related choices can help you reflect and draw a line for yourself to determine what might be driven by shame and what might be fun and worth keeping.

For the next 24 hours (and ideally, over the next week), be especially mindful of the beauty work you do on a regular basis. Answer the following questions in your journal or in conversation with a loved one:

- Does the amount of time, money, and energy I'm investing in my beauty and diet regimens feel appropriate, burdensome, or somewhere in between?

- Could any of my valuable resources be invested in better ways?

- Which parts of my beauty routine and habits do I rely on to look or feel like "myself" or the best version of "myself"?

- Can I explore cutting any of them down or out of my life, just to see how it feels?

- Is there anything I especially enjoy or appreciate about my beauty routine?

- Where do I draw the line between what is creative and fun in my beauty work and what is driven by shame, self-consciousness, and wanting to live up to a hoped-for ideal?

- Am I happy with where that line is drawn, or could I consider setting a new boundary for my beauty work or diet?

As you reflect on your inventory answers, you can decide what parts of your routine might be motivated by shame and a feeling of necessity and what is more creative, playful, and based in self-expression. Consider what you might benefit from spending less time, money, and energy on and what you can do with that time instead. If you do see opportunities to make a new choice or prove that shame-based decision wrong (you are still you without that beauty choice!), it's time to implement some changes to your routine that will benefit you now and in the future.

4

Uniting Instead of Dividing

Lesson 4.1 Divided By Body Ideals

"In a world that revolves around objectification, we see bodies—our own and others'—as things to be admired and appraised and controlled. In our everyday interactions, we cut down others' body images, reinforce and remind each other of our objectifying environment, police each other's bodies, and get pulled or pull others deeper into the waters of objectification with our words and actions. When we focus on others' looks, not only are we perpetuating a culture of objectification, we are also being divided against each other."

—*More Than a Body*, p. 170-171

When you grow up feeling defined by and validated or invalidated based on how you look instead of who you are on a deeper level, it feels natural to make snap judgements about everyone else—for good and bad—based on how they look, too. It is common to cut people down by criticizing their looks and build them up by complimenting their looks. It can be second nature to look at someone and think you know a lot about them based on how they dress, their weight and body shape, and the time (or lack thereof) they put into their appearance. We become the oppressed and the oppressors; the victims of our objectifying culture and the perpetrators enforcing it upon each other.

Your relationship with your parents, as well as your relationship with your own children (if or when you have them) can be complicated by negative self-talk, dieting and diet talk, exercising to achieve aesthetic ideals, and feeling like your family needs to fit certain beauty and body standards. During the formative years of childhood, your caretakers played a deeply impactful role in how you learned to view and relate to your own body.

Your first invitation into the Sea of Objectification may have been your primary caretaker speaking disparagingly about their own body or someone else's. It is likely you internalized that message and learned to see yourself through that same negative view. If they dieted and restricted food, moralizing what was "good" and what was "bad," you probably learned to eat in a similar cycle of binge eating or overeating and restricting to "make up for it." If they used exercise as primarily a way to achieve aesthetic goals or as punishment for what they ate, you may have grown up with this same mentality. Alternatively, you may have had caretakers who were examples of self-love and confidence, which granted you the chance to spend more time as a child comfortably in your body on the shore before stepping into the objectifying waters.

A caretaker's ideas about their own body also creep into their perspective about their child's body—both in a protective way (to help them avoid potential embarrassment or consequences of not fitting certain standards, or to gain the privileges of living up to beauty ideals) and in a critical way (to keep a child in line as a reflection of the caretaker or family). This has a major effect on the relationship dynamic between caretaker and child, creating tension, distrust, fear of judgment or punishment, or even bonding over shared ideals and "flaws." As you work on feeling more comfortable and at home in your body, it is important to consider what body image lessons you learned from your caretakers so you can decide which ones you want to hold on to and which ones you can leave behind.

Challenge for Now
What "Little You" Learned

Using your journal, reflect on the following prompts:

- How did my primary caretaker feel about their body? (If you have more than one, feel free to include them. You may take cues from their words about themself or others, their relationship with food, whether they participated in activities or sat on the sidelines due to shame, etc.).

- How did my primary caretaker feel about my body? (You may take cues from what they said to you, how they treated you, how they talked about or treated others in relation to you, etc.).

- How do the lessons you learned from your primary caretaker impact your relationship with your body today?

- Which lessons and beliefs about bodies from your caretaker do you want to keep and pass on?

- Which lessons and beliefs about bodies from your caretaker do you want to work on rejecting?

- How did your primary caretaker's relationship with their body impact your personal relationship with each other as people? How might it have affected your dynamic together? How has it changed or evolved over time?

| Lesson 4.2 |

Better Than Body Compliments

"Even when we feel united with other girls and women and our interactions with each other are free from the divisions caused by competitiveness and self-comparison, we still make things difficult for each other...Any comment about appearance functions as a little splash—a friendly, non-aggressive, well-intentioned splash—that nevertheless instantly directs your attention back to the waters of objectification, where you are defined by how you appear over anything else."

—*More Than a Body*, p. 171-172

As you navigate this beauty and body-obsessed world with those you love, compliments intended to boost someone's self-esteem can backfire. When they're about bodies, frequent kind words can actually be unkind, as they serve to reinforce beauty as the most valuable asset you have to offer. Both online and face-to-face, looks-based compliments can be a not-so-subtle reminder that you are being looked at and appraised, which can trigger your own self-objectification and lead to a heightened focus on how you look.

For those who spent big parts of their lives being validated and admired for their body or beauty, it can be an especially painful disruption to your body image when your body changes. As you start to gain or lose weight, show signs of aging, face an illness or disability, or other change that pushes you further from the ideals you used to fit, it can be difficult to not receive the validation you used to rely on to feel confident. The upside: Once you realize that appearance compliments don't always work as intended, you can change the way you express your admiration and kindness to people and model how they can do the same for you.

If you are giving a looks-based compliment, we generally advise that people stick to kind words related to someone's creative self-expression over which they have full control (a color they are wearing, a fashion choice, a hairstyle) and avoid validating things people have little control over (like weight and body size). Spending extra time and effort to validate people for who they are beyond their bodies will result in greater unity and deeper relationships from which we can all benefit.

Challenge for Now
Rerouting Others' Compliments

When we receive looks-based compliments—particularly those around body size and weight—it is helpful to have a mental script ready to re-route the well-meaning person kindly but firmly toward more inclusive future conversation or a change of subject. This script can also be modified for parents or caretakers with children who are often on the receiving end of appearance-oriented comments.

Imagine a specific person you are likely to interact with as you draft this script. Record it in your journal or in your phone notes to use later. Feel free to tailor it for your individual needs, but be sure to include the following points:

Acknowledge the Kind Intent:
- "Thank you for the compliment"
- "I appreciate you"

Lead with Vulnerability:
- "To be honest, I'm actually working on paying less attention to my looks. I've started to notice how much time I've spent thinking about my appearance and realizing how draining/expensive/unfulfilling it is."
- "I know you weren't aware, but my daughter/family member/friend is struggling with her body image, so I am trying to shift our focus to how we feel and what we do instead of how we look."

Call to Action:
- "Would you want to join me in this? I have a book I'd love to share with you about body image/I'll share a post with you that resonated with me."
- "I am wondering if you could help me with this. Instead of compliments about weight/body/beauty that keep us focused on those things, I'm trying to think more deeply about the compliments I give. It's harder than I thought but more meaningful! Want to join me?"

- "I want to help my [daughter/family member/friend] see her value beyond her beauty, and it would mean a lot for her to also hear how kind/smart/funny/talented she is from people like you who care about her."

- "You should have her tell you how her soccer game went/what she's reading/what she did for her birthday."

Challenge for Now
Rerouting Your Compliments

If you are someone who often compliments people on their appearance (which so many of us do, and it is always with the best of intentions), take some time now to consciously prepare for how you might re-route your compliments to be more holistic and less looks-centered.

- Who you are likely to see in the coming days—colleagues, friends, family, or acquaintances?

- Think of one or two specific people and imagine what your automatic, default compliments to them might sound like.

- Would those compliments reflect what you value most about them? If not, let's dig a little deeper.

- Would those compliments relate to weight loss or thinness? If so, please consider avoiding this topic entirely. (See *More Than a Body*, p. 195-196, for more on why this is such a risky and often harmful comment choice.)

- What has this person been up to? What have they been dealing with or participating in? Consider being prepared with a specific question or two that shows you care and have been thinking about them.

- What do you really appreciate about this person? Even if you want to appreciate a choice they've made in clothing or a haircut or some other surface-level attribute, do your best to pair it with a deeper compliment about what you really value about them. What have they done that impressed you, helped you or someone else, or demonstrated some positive characteristic you admire?

Lesson 4.3	United with Compassion

"You can stop seeing others as competition or threats and instead see allies, friends, and helpers. You can bond with women you used to judge as too vain, too immodest, too fat, too beautiful. You can take your mom's comment about your body and recognize her internalized objectification without internalizing it yourself. You can see the pain and shame of women being masked by products, procedures, and diets and validate them for more than their 'improved' appearances. You can stop seeing other women as objects to be evaluated, sexy threats to your relationship, or alluring distractions to your sons, and instead see all people as full humans with full agency."

—*More Than a Body*, p. 185

It is perfectly normal to feel triggered by people you know and love in real life who, for one reason or another, cause you to feel less than or to feel insecure in your relationship or in your own body. The key to alleviating these feelings that make you want to compete, criticize, and isolate yourself from others is to recognize what you share: Your common humanity. You share the experience of navigating an objectifying environment, regardless of how different you might look or act, your background, your relationship status, or any other descriptor you choose. This shared experience and the accompanying pain of self-objectification, body shame, violence and the threat of violence, lost time, energy and resources spent on the pursuit of beauty can be an entry point to compassion and connection.

Challenge for Now
Recognizing Our Common Humanity

Devote 5-10 minutes to the following practice:

- Identify someone you know in real life who triggers you to compare yourself or causes you to feel self-conscious of your appearance or otherwise feel less than when they are around. This person might be totally oblivious to the effect they have on you, or it might be someone who tries to provoke insecurity or draw attention to themselves at the expense of others. (In our research, "my sister-in-law" was the most common example people identified as a trigger to their body anxiety.)

- Sitting or lying down in silence, envision this person in your mind. Picture what it is about this person that tends to make you feel jealous, threatened, annoyed, or self-conscious. What do they do or say that triggers these negative feelings for you? Is your insecurity sparked by the ways other people treat them or interact with them?

- Instead of the annoyance, anxiety, or self-comparison you usually feel when you see them, you are now willing to approach this visualization being disarmed, feeling only curiosity and openness to understand them.

- Imagine you are watching a screening of their life— not a glamorous highlight reel you might see on social media, but an actual, realistic day-to-day montage of what they have experienced.

- You first see them as a little kid, home with their family, experiencing all the ups and downs of growing up and dealing with sickness, injuries, family conflict, loss, and insecurity, as well as happiness, learning, safety, new skills, and positive relationships.

- You watch their first exposure to objectification— maybe critical comments from a parent about their growing body, getting assaulted or shouted at by a crude man in public, or receiving mean comments or messages on social media. It could even be the validation and attention they receive for their body and beauty at the expense of their humanity.

- You see them adapt to this new way of thinking about their value—how they watch their reflection, change how they dress to amplify their favorite parts, stop raising their hand in class or drop out of sports, start their first crash diet, spend more time on social media studying the most ideal influencers, the way they seek validation for their looks and sexual appeal.

- You see some of the highest highs in their life—romance, success, love, accomplishments, vacations, and social gatherings and fun events.

- You see some of the lowest lows in their life—loneliness, discouragement, illness, shame, inadequacy, depression, anxiety, and loss.

As the film concludes, consider the following questions:

- Do you feel like you have more clues to understand why they might do things that trigger you?

- Is there a chance you may have inadvertently objectified them, judging their appearance, or the choices they make relating to their looks or sex appeal?

- Is it possible that their choices or behaviors that you disagree with are their way to navigate the objectifying environment we all face?

- What do you have in common with them?

- How might this visualization help you change how you feel or interact with them in the future?

Lesson 4.4

Dressing for the Wearer, Not the Watcher

"Girls learn the most important thing about them is how they look.

Boys learn the most important thing about girls is how they look.

Girls look at themselves.

Boys look at girls.

Girls are held responsible for boys looking at them.

Girls change how they look.

Boys keep looking.

The problem isn't how girls look.

The problem is how everyone looks at girls."

—*More Than a Body*, p. 178

Secular dress codes and religious modesty rules that involve ultra-specific dress codes for only girls and women don't prevent anyone from being perceived as sexual objects—they reinforce it. They turn girls and women into parts instead of people, asking them and everyone looking at them to hyperfocus on each part to be covered. Amid these unyielding currents and waves of objectification, girls and women are held accountable not only for how they present themselves, but for how they are perceived by everyone else. This is a burden no one should be required to bear.

Where dress codes or rules of appropriate dress are needed, we recommend establishing guidelines that prioritize how people feel in their clothing and in their own bodies—not how others see them or feel about what they see. We can all help girls, women, and people of all genders to see and experience themselves as more than bodies by teaching them to consciously consider the ways their clothing choices affect their own self-perceptions, self-consciousness, and ability to function. Prioritizing the wearer instead of the watcher is the compassionate, reasonable approach to help people take control of their own thoughts and actions.

 Challenge for Now
Dressing For You

As you consider the ways so many dress codes and modesty rules inadvertently sexualize and objectify girls and women, we challenge you to create a personal set of rules or guidelines that help you prioritize how you feel in your clothing, regardless of how anyone else might perceive you. For this exercise, consider how the clothing you choose to wear impacts your relationship with your body. In your journal, reflect on the following prompts:

- What factors do I consider when choosing what clothing to buy or what to wear?

- In general, do my clothing choices help or hinder my ability to experience my body as an instrument for my use instead of an ornament to be admired? In other words, do my clothes keep me preoccupied with how my body looks by requiring adjustment, staying sucked in or posed in certain positions to look right? Or do they help me stay focused on other things by not requiring my attention?

- Which outfits or items of clothing do I feel most "instrumental" in, or most comfortable, at ease, and at home in my body while going about my life?

- Which outfits or items of clothing do I feel most "ornamental" in, or most fixated on how I look?

- Do I wear anything that physically hurts me? (Clothes that are too tight, heels, compression underwear, etc.)

- Do I ever feel pressured to wear clothing I don't actually feel comfortable wearing? (For the sake of trends or fashion, sex appeal, religion, pressure from loved ones, work requirements, etc.)

- If so, are there ways I can avoid or modify those clothing choices to be more comfortable?

- Do I hold myself back from wearing certain clothing I really want to wear because I am afraid of how others will perceive me or judge me?

- If so, and if those clothing choices are appropriate for the setting you have in mind, are you willing to challenge yourself to wear them and see how you feel?

- Do I consciously or subconsciously impose my own subjective ideas of appropriate dress on others (including colleagues, family members, friends or even strangers)?

Use your answers to these questions to inform your new dress code. Moving forward, what will you prioritize when you are shopping and getting dressed, and what will you throw out? What values will guide your dress code? How will you prioritize yourself as the wearer of the clothing instead of the imaginary viewer of your wardrobe?

Summary

Chapter 4
Uniting Instead
of Dividing

When we can learn to see ourselves and everyone else as more than bodies, we can see our true humanity, in all its complexity. Our bonds and networks will be stronger, deeper, and more satisfying as we join together instead of pushing each other away. Whether it's with our original caretakers, family members, friends, colleagues, or strangers, we can use truth and vulnerability to connect instead of living in lonely isolation. Together, we can uproot objectification, and, in its place, we can find opportunities to rise with resilience together.

 Challenge for Later
Helping Kids Choose Their Clothes

If you are a caretaker, you have the opportunity to help your children prioritize their own comfort, ability to function, and self-expression in the clothing they wear as opposed to the pressure they may feel to dress to be attractive and on-trend. While it might feel necessary to protect your child from a hyper-sexualized culture by enforcing a hyper-specific dress code, we caution that you may be inadvertently sexualizing her and teaching her to self-objectify as a collection of parts.

For young children:

- Dress them for functionality, not to be decorative. Prioritize practicality over pretty to help them understand the instrumental value of their bodies. From infancy, make sure their clothes are functional and comfortable.

- Recognize the differences between boys' and girls' clothing options that reinforce the idea that girls are here to be cute, and boys are here to be active or smart or strong. Choose gender-neutral items or be willing to shop in the boys' section if the girls' choices are less functional.

- Introduce your kids to our life-changing mantra: My body is an instrument, not an ornament. Ask them to memorize it and repeat it when they are able to do so. Help them understand their bodies as instruments for their use and experience first—not as ornaments to be looked at and judged.

- When they are getting dressed or trying on clothing, ask them questions: How do you feel? Is it stretchy and roomy enough? Is it comfortable or does anything hurt? Can you move with ease? Do your shoes allow you to play and run and climb?

For older children:

- Teach them to be conscious and critical of the ways they may have learned to view and value themselves as objects to be looked at, and how this might influence their clothing choices (and the trending styles of clothing available to them).

- Talk to them about self-objectification. Research on young women shows us that wearing body-baring and tight clothing leads to greater states of self-consciousness, body shame, negative mood, and general distraction. With this in mind, you can help them learn to think about making clothing choices that prioritize their own comfort, experience, and expression rather than only relying on increasing their sexual appeal or popularity.

- Ask them to make clothing decisions with the following questions in mind: Which clothes make you feel your most comfortable and least preoccupied with your appearance? Which clothes leave you constantly adjusting and monitoring yourself?

Challenge for Later
Reviewing Dress Codes

Most institutions require their employees, students, visitors, or clients to adhere to a dress code of some sort. Let's investigate the rules for dress and appearance at the institutions of which you are a part to determine whether any parts could be revised and revisited to better serve all members of the community.

Step 1: Find your dress code online or in a handbook or guiding document.

Step 2: Consider the following questions:

- Does the dress code specify rules based on gender? If so, what are the rules and how do they differ based on gender?

- What are the consequences of breaking the rules of appropriate dress?

- Do some groups bear more responsibility for others' perceptions or actions than other groups?

- Are there things you would flag in this dress code as sexually objectifying or otherwise unequal, sexist, racist, harmful, or unnecessary? Why?

Step 3: If you feel compelled, request a meeting with church leadership, a member of the school board, administration, or human resources (HR) team to discuss potential revisions to the dress code to be more inclusive. Feel free to use excerpts from *More Than a Body* to help guide the conversation.

5 Reclaiming Health and Fitness for Yourself

Lesson 5.1 See More in Your Health

"The words diet and weight loss may be out of fashion in many circles, but their reign as the most important factors in people's ideas about health has not ended. Regardless of how these appearance-focused ideals are packaged, we can all learn to see through the illusions and see more in our health than the outsider's perspective we've adopted to evaluate ourselves. Just like we need to redefine beauty in ways that are better for our health, we need to redefine health in ways that have nothing to do with beauty."

—*More Than a Body*, p. 216

Take a look back at the Self-objectification Score (SOS) Quiz in the beginning of this workbook—specifically questions D and M, which focused on how you think about your own health and fitness. Did your answers emphasize weight, size, or appearance like most of the women in our research? It's a natural thought process for us to do so because our culture's ideals about fitness and beauty are so intertwined that they sound and look almost exactly the same—always with a major emphasis on thinness and youth, looking "toned" and "firm" or with visible muscle definition, with flat stomachs and rounded bottoms, low or no body fat, and smooth, tight skin.

We know it is nearly impossible to feel positively toward your body when you're judging it according to society's beauty standards, and the same holds true for judging our health. The women in our studies who felt negatively toward their bodies overwhelmingly believed health and fitness were impossible for them to attain or could only be attained with extreme deprivation and sacrifice. This focus on thinness and other beauty ideals that are unreachable for most people is tragic, and only leads to worse health outcomes—including cycles of restricting and bingeing, disordered eating, compulsive overexercising, use of unregulated and dubious supplements, and substance use disorders involving alcohol and drugs, whether prescription, over the counter, or illegal.

A key takeaway from Chapter 5 of *More Than a Body* is that your BMI and weight do not define your worth, and they do not define your health, either. In the following lessons, we will ask you to take a deeper look at your ideas of healthy and fit—how those ideas might have been warped and twisted by objectification, how to un-warp and un-twist those ideas, and create a more personalized understanding of what health and fitness might mean for you.

Challenge for Now
Reflecting on Health and Fitness

Using your journal, reflect on the following questions:

- Have you or others (including parents or caretakers, medical professionals, coaches, etc.) ever judged your health and fitness according to measures like weight, Body Mass Index (BMI), size measurements, body fat percentage, or dress size? (List any that apply from your past or present.)

- Looking back, do you believe these measurements were an accurate reflection of your health and fitness at the time?

- How have these measurements impacted you in terms of how you felt about your body and your health or fitness?

- How have these measurements impacted the ways you have treated your body?

- How does it feel to consider that these measurements (weight, BMI, size) are not accurate or effective at helping you understand your health and fitness, according to extensive research that has spanned decades?

- How do you think your feelings about your body or your choices relating to your body throughout your life would have changed if you knew that your weight, size, and BMI were not very important in judging your health?

Next, take a few minutes to honestly reflect on your health without focusing on your weight, shape, or appearance.

- Generally, how do you feel in your daily life? How do you feel when you wake up in the morning, play with kids, walk down the street, take the stairs, or carry groceries inside? Does your body serve you how you want it to? Are you able to do the activities and tasks you want or need to do in your life without too much of a struggle, or ending up in pain due to lack of cardiovascular fitness or muscle strength?

- Are you satisfied with the amount of energy you have on a typical day, or are you more tired and sluggish than you would like?

- Do you feel generally well, or do you feel that something might be out of balance inside your body— nutritionally, digestively, hormonally, metabolically, cardiovascularly, or in another way that affects your physical well-being?

With all of this in mind, do you feel you have a good sense for your overall health status right now? If not, or if you are unsure, we recommend visiting a doctor or trusted medical professional who can help you understand your health from within.

| Lesson 5.2 |

Find Better Fitspiration

"When you learn to see more in yourself and your health, you see that the look of your body does not always correlate with your health or happiness. It's just not the way our bodies or our lives work. Many people run marathons; complete triathlons; swim for miles; dance for hours; have balanced eating habits and perfect blood pressure, cholesterol, blood sugar, and resting heart rates and good cardiovascular health—and still don't have a body you would ever see in a fitness magazine or even a typical 'after' photo. Alternatively, lots of people go to unhealthy extremes like disordered eating, over-exercising, using steroids and unsafe diet pills, and cosmetic surgery to achieve the look of health."

—*More Than a Body*, p. 225

When pursuing fitness goals or trying to improve our health, lots of people seek motivation online or from popular "fitspo" (i.e. fitness inspiration) influencers and pros. The problem is that most of them tend to look almost exactly the same, fitting all the typical sexualized ideals from mainstream media and advertising, despite real-life fit and healthy people's bodies reflecting a huge spectrum of shapes, sizes, and looks. Sometimes our inspiration comes from seeing dramatic before-and-after photos that are almost always advertising radical weight loss solutions, often from people you know in real life or follow online.

With such one-dimensional, appearance-driven ideas about wellness surrounding us, it's no wonder so many of us are duped into equating our health with our hotness. Then, when our attempts to reach fitness goals or improve our health don't change our bodies in the ways we were led to believe they would, we're left feeling discouraged and depressed. And it's especially troubling when that frustration and feeling of failure leads us to extremes like overexertion, disordered eating, substance use disorders, or giving up and becoming more sedentary—all of which happen way too often.

Fortunately, taking a critical look at what we might have considered "fitspo" or motivational in the past can help us untangle our ideas about beauty from our ideas about fitness, and then shift our goals to be more achievable and health-promoting. We can start by taking a more compassionate approach to looking at the past images of ourselves we may have idealized while seeking fitness inspiration.

Challenge for Now
Revisiting Past Pics

Many of us scroll or flip through old photos or videos of ourselves and are struck with the thought, "I wish I still looked like that." Do you have a past photo of yourself you have idealized as your "body goals?" Or a photo you have considered an "after" in a before-and-after body transformation period when you were intentionally trying to change your appearance? If so, please find it and reflect on the following questions as you look at it.

- How did I feel about my body and myself at that time?

- What was happening in my life at that time?

- How much of my time, energy, money, or attention revolved around my appearance at that time?

- What have I experienced in my life since then? What ups, downs, and changes have I been through in the months or years since then?

- What do I wish I felt about my body and myself at that time?

- What if, in 10 years, I look back at my body from today and feel the same as I do now, looking back on this past version of myself? What might it change about how I think about my body or treat myself today?

| Lesson 5.3 |

Be an Instrument, Not an Ornament

"My body is an instrument, not an ornament. This mantra shifts your outlook from form to function and feeling, from an outsider-focused view to an insider knowledge. Our bodies are instruments for our own personal use, experience, and benefit—not ornaments to be admired. At first, the idea of giving up on achieving weight goals and aesthetic ideals might make you feel like you are giving up on your health or your body. The reality is, letting go of aesthetic goals frees you up to find a new, more effective and empowering way of understanding and experiencing health and fitness for yourself."

—*More Than a Body*, p.236-237

The overwhelming takeaway from research on weight, mortality, and fitness is that people should be focusing on fitness rather than fatness. Instead of relying on weight or BMI, focusing on healthy behaviors like increasing physical activity is key to improving health. Focus on how you feel and what you do rather than how you look. We call this an "instrumental" view of bodies and fitness, rather than an "ornamental" one. With this perspective, you can better understand your health and reconnect with your body by focusing on behavior over beauty, actions over aesthetics, on being an active subject rather than a passive object to be looked at.

This paradigm shift makes health improvement so much more achievable than the body ideals we've been trained to associate with fitness. Our study participants who felt hopeless about ever achieving health or fitness drastically increased their confidence in their ability to do so after learning to redefine health and fitness without objectified body ideals.

Keep in mind that while there are lots of ways we are in control of our health and behaviors, our health is determined by so many variables outside our control—from where we were born and our socioeconomic status to genetics and environmental factors. We don't get to decide if we are always healthy or able-bodied or free from illness or disease, and our bodies won't always (or maybe ever) be perfect instruments, despite our best efforts. We aim to do the best with the bodies and capabilities we have, knowing that regardless of any limitations and frustrations, our bodies are still instruments, not ornaments.

Challenge for Now
Setting Instrumental Goals

How do you avoid setting objectified fitness goals that keep you focused on your body as an ornament rather than an instrument? The difference can be pretty difficult to tease out if you've been immersed in appearance-focused thinking about your health. Using your journal, reflect on the following questions:

- What have my past fitness goals sounded like? (Share examples of resolutions, milestones, or other body- and health-related aspirations.)

- For each goal, consider the question: Is this goal asking me to measure my fatness or my fitness? (If it's measuring fatness, your goal will be visual and literally, physically, measurable—pounds, inches, dress sizes, muscle definition or tone, BMI score. If it's measuring fitness, your goal will be based on what you want to feel, what you want to do and experience, or what you want your medical or lab test results to reveal.)

- How can I reframe these goals or set brand new ones that focus on using my body as an instrument, not viewing it as an ornament?

Take a few minutes to ponder on what you really want to gain, improve, or experience in relation to your health or fitness. Rewrite your goals with this in mind. (For example, climb X flights of stairs without being winded, walk or run a certain distance or period of time each week, do X repetitions of bicep curls or squats with X pounds, get your heart rate in a certain range for X minutes every day, rebuild strength in an area after an injury or operation, decrease your blood pressure or cholesterol, leveling out your blood sugar, compete in a race or other challenge, etc.)

Keep these new goals somewhere you can revisit them often, like the notes on your phone or a note in your home.

Lesson 5.4

A Better Kind of Before and After

"When you are mindful of what health choices mean and feel like in your life, trying to prove or demonstrate that hard work and dedication with a simple photo of your body is doing a disservice to what you are actually accomplishing. What if instead of thinking of yourself in static, reductive terms of 'before' or 'after,' you thought of yourself as in between those two points: during. Any photo you take of yourself right now is just a 'during' shot, captured as you experience your ever-evolving, ever-learning existence."

—*More Than a Body*, p. 228-229

To reclaim our definitions of health while also aspiring for more achievable and fulfilling fitness goals, we need to take a much more personalized approach. There is no one-size-fits-all recipe for wellness, so it's time to define it for ourselves. Most importantly, we need to get objectification out of the way and get the focus back inside our bodies.

Challenge for Now
Redefining Your Before and After

Review the following before-and-after checklist and star or write down each item that pertains to you.

BEFORE reclaiming health and fitness for myself, I've done these things that I now plan to stop doing:

- Weighing myself or measuring my body regularly.

- Meticulously tracking the number of calories, carbohydrates, sugars, or fats I eat (unless medically necessary for diabetes or other blood sugar management).

- Taking and keeping "before" photos of myself to mark a starting point in a body transformation.

- Regularly looking back at past images of myself to compare my body or motivate myself.

- Following fitness influencers, models, before-and-after advertisers, or celebrities with idealized bodies for inspiration.

- Exercising as punishment for what I've eaten or how much I dislike my body.

- Staring at or monitoring my reflection in the mirror the whole time I exercise.

- Wearing aesthetically pleasing but uncomfortable or revealing clothing to work out that keeps me constantly adjusting, sucking in, and fixating on my appearance.

- Judging my health according to my BMI or dress size.

- Avoiding physical activity or getting outside my comfort zone because of self-consciousness about my body (which makes it much worse!).

- Restricting foods or food groups in an attempt to shrink my body (which backfires 100% of the time and leads to binge eating—my body's natural response to the threat of starvation).

AFTER reclaiming health and fitness for myself, I plan to do these things:

- Where possible, talk to a doctor or trusted medical professional about wanting to really understand my health from within, and get lab tests, blood panels, and other indicators of my health status.

- Delete or discard any old records I've kept of my weight, size, or food restriction.

- Delete or discard any "before" photos intended to mark a body transformation or guilt me into changing my body.

- Seek out and follow fitness advocates or athletes who don't focus on looks, weight, or idealized bodies, and who represent and highlight body diversity in sports and exercise.

- Push through any feelings of "too fat to exercise" or temptation to hide due to not looking good enough to participate in classes, sports, public physical activity, or other movement that would be beneficial for my health and body image.

- Regularly reflect on and express gratitude and appreciation for all the ways my body is instrumental, regardless of ability, illness, or other limitations.

- Learn about intuitive eating (start with the pioneers of the practice—registered dietitians and authors Evelyn Tribole and Elyse Resch) instead of dieting.

- Be conscious of the powerful ways my genetics, environment, upbringing, socioeconomic status, and so many other factors outside my control affect my body and health and build compassion for myself and others who face obstacles to good health.

Summary

Chapter 5
Reclaiming Health and Fitness for Yourself

When you can see more in your health than the numbers and appearance ideals you might have been trained to focus on, your body can become an instrument for your own use and experience rather than an ornament to be admired, fixed, and judged. With that shift in perspective, you can have greater access to your own physical power that comes through experiencing your body from the inside, not the outside.

 Challenge for Later
Motivating Movement

Though most fitspo in advertising relies on an objectified idea of fitness, research shows us there are positive sources of fitspo that can help us decrease self-objectifying thoughts. One of the best sources of this positive fitspiration is by watching female athletes in action.

Take a few minutes to seek out and reflect on videos or images of a variety of female athletes amid their sport or physical challenge—whether streaming on social media or a video platform, live TV, or still photos from a game or competition. Good examples include soccer players, competitive weightlifters, track and field athletes, runners at a 10k or marathon finish line, or any competitive team sport that does not rely on aesthetics in scoring (e.g. ice skating, dance, cheer).

Reflect on the following questions during or after viewing:

- How does it feel to see athletes in movement, focused on a task, compared to seeing fitness models or influencers in videos or images that are strategically posed to emphasize their sexual appeal?

- What do I most notice and admire about these athletes and their performance?

- If this has a positive impact on how I think about my own goals or motivation, how can I incorporate this type of imagery or fitspo into my life more regularly? (For example, subscribing to or following certain teams, channels, hashtags, or feeds, learning or participating in certain activities or sports, observing athletes or teams competing near you, taking kids or friends to a game, etc.)

Challenge for Later
Advocating for Yourself with Others

As we work to untangle our ideas of health from our ideas of beauty, we need to prepare to speak up and potentially have difficult conversations in order to advocate for ourselves and others. Whether talking with a healthcare professional, parent or family member, friend, or colleague, you will likely run into conversations with well-meaning people who focus on fatness instead of fitness. It helps to have a few talking points in mind.

In your journal, take notes of talking points you'd like to implement. Here is what we suggest:

- Be open that you are working to avoid focusing on weight, size, and any other appearance-oriented goals because you've found they are discouraging or actually get in the way of your healthy choices. You are prioritizing your health or fitness, and you have learned that your weight and appearance aren't accurate reflections of that.

- If you're comfortable, be vulnerable about what you or a loved one have faced because of feeling defined by your appearance, whether it is disordered eating, over-exercising, substance use disorders, self-harm, mental health challenges, feeling compelled to hide, or other challenges that got in the way of your health and fitness.

- If they express any confusion or are interested in learning more, tell them about *More Than a Body*, recommend an article, share a social media post, or tell them there's a huge body of research that shows physical activity is a better indicator of a person's fitness than their weight or size (look up Glenn A. Gaesser, PhD, and those he cites).

- Ask for their help to keep the focus on how you feel and what you are doing instead of how you look or recruit them to join you in working on shifting your focus. You could even share our mantra—"My body is an instrument, not an ornament"—to see if it resonates.

- If you're talking with a healthcare professional, let them know you would like to opt out of the weigh-in, or if that isn't possible, tell them you do not want to see or hear about your weight.

- Ask your healthcare provider for help to get greater insights into your health, including your blood pressure, resting heart rate, blood sugar levels, cholesterol, risk factors for illness or disease, and even just feedback on your lifestyle and habits or how you're feeling about your overall wellness. Your provider can help you understand what your ideal internal measures of health might be, and what you can adjust to achieve those goals.

- If they can't help, or they aren't willing to skip the weight discussion, it is time to look for a new healthcare provider, if possible.

Challenge for Later

Using Your Body as An Instrument

Getting involved in any kind of athletics or enjoyable physi-cal activity is a practical way to shift your perspective toward what you are doing and feeling instead of how you look or what you weigh. You will also benefit from the endorphins and flow state that can result from movement. Test out what it feels like to focus on your instrumental body internally rather than how exercise might impact you externally. You can do this by finding any type of movement you enjoy and doing it mindfully and consciously while taking inventory of what you experience during it.

Take some time in the next few days to participate in a physical activity of your choice. As you walk, swim, dance, do yoga, lift weights, or whatever you are able to do, consider the following questions:

- How does it feel to move my body in this way?

- Am I enjoying what I'm doing, or does this feel like a punishment?

- What effects do I want this activity or movement to have on me and my body?

- For each of those effects, honestly consider whether they are instrumental (strengthening muscles, building endurance, improving circulation, stress or pain relief, etc.) or ornamental (shrinking any parts, growing glutes to look better in leggings, etc.).

- What causes my attention to slip away to focus on how I look? (Mirrors, people watching you, or uncomfortable clothing, including body-baring or restricting clothing, might be examples of factors that trigger you to self-objectify during physical activity.)

- How can I decrease or avoid triggers to my self-objectification during this activity? (Consider choosing different locations in the gym or studio where you are less likely to watch your reflection, experiment with different clothing choices, speak with a coach or instructor about getting the focus off how you look and onto how you feel, increasing your pace or listening to upbeat music to get you in the zone, etc.)

If or when your attention goes to how you appear, work to push it back to what you are doing or experiencing. If you catch your mind worrying how your arms look while they jiggle each time you move them or how you might look to that stranger in front of you, repeat a mantra to yourself that resonates with you. For example, "My body is an instrument, not an ornament" or "I am not here to be looked at."

Then, shift your attention to how it feels to move the way you are moving. Engage each of your senses in a conscious way. What does the air feel like on your skin and moving in and out of your lungs? What do you appreciate about this moment, how you're feeling, or what you're doing? Do you feel any changes in your mood or energy level throughout this movement?

6 Reuniting

Choosing Resilience

"As you have lived your life and faced difficulties and been changed (for better or worse) by them, you have been learning all along the way. You bring all of that experience and knowledge into your next body image disruption, and the next, and the next, and the next. That accumulation of understanding, skills, and sensitivities will buoy you up and power you forward as you find new ways to live and understand your body image and yourself. With those personal sources of wisdom and strength in tow, you can consciously and systematically practice your new skills for body image resilience in order to get you back home to yourself."

—*More Than a Body*, p. 301-302

You have likely spent too much time navigating the dangerous waters of objectification in your comfort zone life raft, being battered by waves of disruption that leave you sinking in shame or coping in ways that never get you to safety. The pain of body shame might always sting, but that sting can be the prompting to come back to yourself instead of coping in ways that sink you deeper into shame. That pain can propel you into action through practicing your skills for body image resilience. Rather than adapting to your body shame by clinging to your comfort zone, you can turn toward what you know about yourself and your capacity for growth and change. You can feel empowered to leave your old ways of coping behind because now you know there is a pathway out of this vicious cycle and toward the full, embodied life you deserve.

It is impossible to avoid waves of body image disruption because of this objectifying environment that surrounds you, but now your response to those waves can help you instead of hurt you. Equipped with your knowledge and skills for resilience—from media literacy and self-compassion to reconnecting with yourself and redefining health—you can face any wave of disruption and ensure it is an enabling one. Choose to make any wave of body shame into a reminder of what you're up against. Let it remind you to come back home to yourself by propelling you toward your new path: rising with body image resilience.

Challenge for Now
Riding the Waves of Disruption

Of the scenarios below, circle or star those that would be considered Waves of Body Image Disruption in your life:

- You go on a date with someone you're interested in who tells you they aren't attracted to you.

- You try on a pair of jeans or shirt you used to wear, and it is too tight.

- A loved one you are close to criticizes your appearance.

- You are asked to give a presentation to a large group of people in person.

- You are tagged in a group photo or video where you don't like how you look.

- You go to a family function or social gathering where you see a person who triggers your self-comparison.

- You deal with an injury or illness that prevents you from doing your normal fitness regimen or changes your appearance.

- You have the opportunity to go swimming with a group of people you don't know well.

- Your high school or college reunion is coming up.

- You are invited to a formal, black-tie event.

- Your romantic partner makes a comment about someone else's attractiveness.

- Your parents or in-laws have scheduled family photos that include you.

For those scenarios you circled or starred, choose the two or three that you would find most disruptive to your body image, or that would typically cause you to feel the most shame or body anxiety, and write them in your journal.

For each scenario, reflect in writing on the skills you've practiced throughout this workbook that you could use to respond to the disruption.

How could that disruption remind you to push back against objectification and come back to your body as your home instead of your enemy? In other words, how can you make it an enabling disruption that helps you flex your resilience muscle (rather than sinking into shame or coping by hiding or fixing like you may have in the past)?

What future waves of body image disruption are you anticipating, or could you see yourself facing in the future? How can you plan to respond with resilience in the face of these disruptions?

If you need reminders, feel free to flip back through this workbook or your journal.

| Lesson 6.2 |

The Reunion

"To be 'more than a body' is to be whole, to be at one with who you are and always were. It is a reunion. It is self-actualization. It is the highest form of self-love and self-compassion in action because you are embracing yourself, regardless of how you appear. You are embracing and finding deep meaning and purpose in what you and your body have been through, and what you will go through in the future …You won't be divided against your body again. Instead, the pain you experience is an opportunity to reconnect with yourself, to feel yourself slip away, and to know how you can return, more resilient and whole."

—*More Than a Body*, p. 294-295

Regardless of where you are starting right now, you have the opportunity to step into the brave revolution of rising with body image resilience. This is the capacity and skill set you need to survive the waters of objectification and reconnect with the sense of self you started with as a carefree kid. When pursuing out-of-reach body goals and constant sinking, hiding, or fixing have left you stranded, your new skills for rising with body image resilience have propelled you toward a new destination. It is in the distance, beyond the waves, and it might even look familiar, because it's where you started this whole journey: More Than a Body Beach. It's time to come home.

Challenge for Now
Coming Home

Read the following prompt and then, in a comfortable position, close your eyes for at least five minutes and meditate upon the following imagery:

As you've worked through the challenges in this book, you may have started to recall happy, carefree memories from your childhood. You remember playing on the shores of More Than a Body Beach as a child, peacefully existing in your body without fear or anxiety. At some point, you waded or were pulled into the vast Sea of Objectification, splitting from Little You and watching yourself instead of simply living. Maybe you forgot you ever existed that way at all. Life may have been difficult as you have tried to find joy, confidence, love, and success in an environment that placed such a premium on your appearance. You may have been struggling under the sinking weight of body shame, clinging to your body image comfort zone while cold and wet, exhausted by hiding and fixing.

With your latest wave of disruption, you tapped into new skills and strengths to chart a new course. Now, your ideal destination is peacefully at home in your dynamic body, rather than a fantasy version of yourself that relies on false promises of love, confidence, and fulfillment.

As that wave of disruption propels you forward, you look to the horizon in the distance, and you see dry land. On the shore, you see a figure waving her arms high in the air. She jumps up and down, yelling your name, motioning for you to come to her. As you get closer and the water gets shallower, she reaches out her arms to help you find your footing upon the sturdy ground you haven't felt beneath your feet in years. She looks so familiar. You realize you know her. She is you. Your whole, complex, dynamic, human self, right where she has always been since your identity split and you watched yourself drift off into the waters of objectification. She is Little You from the memories and pictures you love from your past, all grown up. The same body you were born in and grew up in and experienced every second of life in. All the bad, all the good, all the pain and joy and highs and lows. She wraps her arms around you, welcoming you home after your long journey to learn how capable and resilient you really are.

You are home, with wisdom gained from the difficult conditions you have experienced and the strengths you have gained along the way. Your comfort zone demands nothing of you and provides no opportunities for growth and lasting fulfillment. Now, at one with yourself again, you are whole. Welcome home.

In your journal, reflect on this meditative experience. How do you feel? What do you want to remember?

Lesson 6.3

The Privilege
of Opting Out

"Too many of us create arbitrary mile markers for ourselves that determine when we deserve some new experience or thing we've been wanting. Holding on to or even just unconsciously accepting these imaginary 'goal' versions of ourselves is a way we create distance between ourselves and our bodies as well as our fullest lives. We think our 'now' bodies are temporary impostors and our 'future' bodies are who we really are, when we'll really be complete. You can't heal the rift in your identity and reunite with your whole self if you are imagining a future self that isn't even real. Prove yourself wrong. Dash your long-held ideals about your body to pieces. Try to do the thing that makes you burst into tears when you acknowledge that you want to do it—regardless of how you look."

—*More Than a Body*, p. 313-14

It is time to opt out of the endless fight to find your worth and confidence through a rigged system that views and values you as an object to be viewed, used, and discarded. If you resign to live as an ornament to be looked at because it is easier than pushing back on profit-driven ideals and pressures, you are complicit in a system that harms all of us. This system insists upon you, your loved ones, peers, and younger generations growing older with the same limited view of themselves and the same life-long burden (and expenses) to carry by living to be looked at.

If you can see that objectification has impacted your life in negative ways, causing you to spend more time, money, and energy on your appearance than you'd like, but you aren't willing to fight against those forces and opt out of this rigged value system, who will? If it is possible for you to survive without buying into every new beauty ideal, what do you have to lose? And what do you have to gain in its place?

Some of us have more privilege than others to opt out of strict beauty pressures or push back on our own objectification. For those whose jobs depend on them adhering to certain beauty standards (including hairstyles, weight or size requirements, makeup or heels, etc.) and who have few options for other career opportunities, or whose housing or safety are at the mercy of someone who insists upon them fitting particular ideals, they might not have as much leeway or power to push back right now.

But for those of us with secure lifestyles, reliable housing and safety, and few strict demands about our bodies from others with real power over us, we are very unlikely to be putting ourselves at risk by opting out of certain objectifying ideals. It is possible the anxieties and fears we feel about not complying with beauty pressures are exaggerated or outsized compared to what it might feel like in reality. We believe we each have a responsibility to carefully consider our beauty choices and what role they play in contributing to the severe pressure in our environment.

Challenge for Now
Interrogating Your Fears

It is time to critically consider the fear and shame that compels you to work toward certain beauty and body ideals. Using your journal, reflect on the following prompts:

- What, if any, particular ideals can you not imagine parting with? (Examples could include maintaining or pursuing a particular weight or size, body hair removal, hair color, keeping up with fashion trends, lashes and brows, anti-aging products and procedures, cosmetic surgery, etc.)

For the ideals you listed, consider the following questions:

- What are your worst fears about what could happen if you stopped pursuing or maintaining that beauty ideal?

- Are your fears realistic or are they exaggerated?

- What do you think is the most likely or most realistic outcome if you stopped pursuing or maintaining that beauty ideal?

- Do you believe you are capable of dealing with the possible outcomes of opting out or not meeting that beauty ideal? (Even if it's difficult, do you believe you have the skills to navigate it or get help to do so?)

- Which aspects of your life truly depend on you upholding the particular ideals you think you need to meet?

Next, consider the possible benefits of opting out of these particular beauty and body ideals and reflect on them in your journal:

- Could you prove to yourself that you are still "you" without it?

- Could you save money, time, and energy?

- Could you avoid painful procedures and products?

- Could you develop more confidence in yourself?

- Could you discover which people in your life value you for more than your temporary appearance?

- Could you empower anyone in your life to opt out of any beauty ideals?

- Could you be an example to others, including younger people, who might look up to you?

Lesson 6.4

Igniting Your Fire

"Being objectified should be infuriating, and your fury will protect you from accepting and internalizing it...Let those painful emotions fuel your fire to make progress and push for change—in your own life and for others...The collective anger of women who are sick of submitting to dangerous ideals and watching themselves and others be reduced to objects is what we need to make real change."

—More Than a Body, p. 321

It is OK to regret the time, energy, and money you have wasted on beauty and body ideal mirages. It is normal to feel rage about the rampant objectification of women in everything from kids' cartoons to conversation at the dinner table. It is perfectly appropriate to mourn the lack of women in positions of power, the silenced voices of women, the collective loss of unencumbered joy, purpose, fulfillment, and confidence.

When you start speaking up about these things, you will find you are not alone. Ask around and you'll find out that you aren't the only one who is saddened and enraged by it. Don't dismiss these feelings as unproductive or wrong; pay attention to where they are leading you. They are a likely signal that you are undergoing a revolutionary, enabling disruption that is propelling you toward a new, more fulfilling way of living. The objectification you witness and experience in your life can motivate you and remind you to be more of who you are and who you could be. Not doubled, disembodied, and divided, but whole, embodied, and complete.

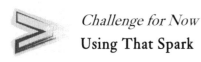

Challenge for Now
Using That Spark

In your journal, answer the following questions:

- As I reflect on the negative impacts of objectification in my life or those around me, what angers or saddens me the most? (Examples: Never seeing anyone who looks like me or my loved ones represented positively in media; violence against girls and women caused by seeing them as objects; kids at school or church being humiliated by dress code violations; realizing how eating disorders, self-harm, or addiction caused by body shame has impacted me or someone I love; acknowledging the lack of female leaders in business and government or how they are judged and degraded; opportunities I've missed out on, etc.)

- Where can I direct these feelings of anger, sadness, resentment, or disgust to make change in my life or beyond? (Examples: Volunteering for or donating to a nonprofit or organization dedicated to supporting victims or survivors of abuse, speaking up when I see objectification happening in places I frequent, calling out demeaning or sexist content online, creating content that reflects what I want to see and what can empower others, having tough conversations with people who perpetuate harmful stereotypes and standards, etc.)

Summary

Chapter 6

Reuniting

Rising with body image resilience is a continuous process—not a one-time accomplishment of finding lasting body love. Building your resilience muscle is totally achievable, practical, and absolutely game changing. Over the past six chapters, you have learned strategies to not only decrease your body shame and self-objectification, but help you improve your relationship with your body every time you do face those waves. You will find yourself venturing back out in the waters of objectification in big and small ways, sometimes drifting out further than you anticipated as you face new pressures from things like pregnancy, aging, illness, and relationships. Now, you will have the ability to recognize when you're prioritizing how you look over how you live, and you have the knowledge and skills you need to return home to your body as you face those waves. You can always come back to the beach.

Remember that every disruption is an opportunity to use the steps and skills you have learned to opt out of self-objectification and opt into your embodied wholeness. Refer to each chapter, lesson, and challenge as often as you need.

Here is a quick recap of each chapter followed by your final challenge:

Chapter 1: Understanding Your Body Image. Each body image disruption can sink you, subdue you, or spark something in you. When the wave hits, investigate what feelings arise. What is prompting your body shame right now? How are you tempted to cope with the shame and discomfort that might be stirred up through this disruption? Now that you can name your disruptions and your responses, you have the power and freedom to choose a new path guided by the knowledge that you are more than a body.

Chapter 2: Critiquing and Creating Your Body Image Environment. Investigate the messages about bodies in your daily life that have created the body image conditions you're in now. What ideals are you consciously or unconsciously holding yourself to? Where did you learn about these ideals? Who or what might benefit from you pinning your shame or hopes to your appearance? How might you create a more habitable environment for your body image?

Chapter 3: Moving from Self-Objectification to Self-Care. Dig deep into your own self-perceptions. How do you feel about yourself? Do you speak and act kindly toward yourself, or look and treat yourself as a critical outsider? Utilize the strategies you have learned to tune into greater purpose and meaning in your life beyond your immediate physical self to reconnect with who you really are and what you are really capable of.

Chapter 4: Uniting Instead of Dividing. You can move forward with others by extending kindness and compassion to all in your path, banding you together to have each other's backs as you navigate rough waters together. How can you practice valuing those in your life for more than just their appearance? What tools can you employ to help you determine whether you are objectifying someone?

Chapter 5: Reclaiming Health and Fitness for Yourself. When you start to feel that your whole value and identity rest on the way your body appears, you can take back your physical power by experiencing your body as an instrument, not an ornament. Measure your health in terms of how you feel, what you can do, and what internal indicators tell you about how your body is doing. What goals can you make that prioritize how you feel, what you can do, and your actual health— not just your appearance?

Chapter 6: Reuniting. With the skills and strategies for resilience you have learned, you are prepared to respond to waves of body image disruption in ways that serve you and teach you more about your strength and capacity. The familiar pain of body shame or self-objectification that used to compel you to cope in unsafe or unfulfilling ways is now an opportunity to respond with greater knowledge, compassion, and power. What can you learn from your disruptions? How can you prepare yourself for future body image burdens? How can you rise with resilience as you face pain and shame?

 Challenge for Now
Revisiting Your SOS

Before you began this workbook, you took the 15-question Self-objectification Score (SOS) quiz starting on page 6. Now that you have completed all the lessons and challenges, re-take that quiz with your current knowledge and skills. When you are finished, add up your score and see how it compares to your original SOS. You might also want to look at individual questions to see where your answers might have shifted over time, paying particular attention to anywhere your answer number increased (for example, your answer went from 2 the first time to 4 the second time). This would demonstrate improvement or a decrease in self-objectifying thoughts or behaviors.

It is totally OK if your score stays in the same category, or you don't see much of a change. Sometimes improvement takes time as you continue to learn and build your skillset, and some of the questions are measuring things we wouldn't expect to change (like the people around you or how you grew up). You might even want to revisit this quiz in the future to check in on how you're doing as you face new challenges and life changes.

The greatest thing you can take away from this process is a new way of seeing and valuing yourself and everyone else—a simple but powerful paradigm shift. You are more than a body; you always have been and you always will be, regardless of how you look or how the world looks at you. Change is already happening. Can you feel it? Every time you show up, speak up, take the lead, share love, accept love, push back, ask questions, and resist the limitations of living as an object to be looked at, you reclaim your power and your very existence. Arm in arm, we are working together to create a kinder, more welcoming, more habitable environment for today and tomorrow and beyond.

See you on the beach.

For more information on Lindsay and Lexie's work,
find them online at morethanabody.org

Made in United States
Troutdale, OR
02/26/2024

17974605R00082